Coping With Eating Disorders

ISSUES
(formerly Issues for the Nineties)

Volume 24

Editor

Craig Donnellan

Independence
Educational Publishers
Cambridge

First published by Independence
PO Box 295
Cambridge CB1 3XP
England

© Craig Donnellan 1998

British Library Cataloguing in Publication Data
Coping With Eating Disorders – (Issues Series)
I. Donnellan, Craig II. Series
616.8'526

ISBN 1 86168 069 4

Printed in Great Britain
City Print Ltd
Milton Keynes

Typeset by
Claire Boyd

Cover
The illustration on the front cover is by
The Attic Publishing Co.

CONTENTS

Chapter One: Eating Disorders

Eating problems	1
What causes eating disorders?	2
My teenage diet hell, by Ginger Spice	3
Anorexia nervosa	4
Bulimia nervosa	6
Anorexia – and the disturbing problem no parent can ignore	8
Fact file	9
How many people have eating and exercise disorders?	11
Helping a friend or a relative	12
Who gets eating disorders?	13
Thin end of the Reg	14
Anorexics 'should be allowed to starve'	15
Slim equals beautiful in the minds of most teenagers	16
15 diet myths exploded	17
Self help – it worked	19
Binge eating disorders	20
Compulsive overeating and binge eating disorder	21
Athletes and eating disorders	23

Chapter Two: Obesity

Obesity	24
Are you a healthy weight?	26
Chunky chaps	27
It's not how fat a fellow is, it's where he's fat	28
Physical activity and weight control	29
Meat eaters are more likely to be obese	31
The real reason so many of us are overweight	32
At last, a little extra weight is growing on us	33
The balance of good health	34
America is big loser in battle of the bulge	35
If you are overweight	36
Worries about weight	37
Slimming foods slow to shape up	38
Let children eat crisps, says doctor	40
Additional resources	41
Index	42
Web site information	43
Acknowledgements	44

Introduction

Coping With Eating Disorders is the twenty-fourth volume in the series: **Issues**. The aim of this series is to offer up-to-date information about important issues in our world.

Coping With Eating Disorders looks at anorexia, bulimia and obesity.

The information comes from a wide variety of sources and includes:
Government reports and statistics
Newspaper reports and features
Magazine articles and surveys
Literature from lobby groups
and charitable organisations.

It is hoped that, as you read about the many aspects of the issues explored in this book, you will critically evaluate the information presented. It is important that you decide whether you are being presented with facts or opinions. Does the writer give a biased or an unbiased report? If an opinion is being expressed, do you agree with the writer?

Coping With Eating Disorders offers a useful starting-point for those who need convenient access to information about the many issues involved. However, it is only a starting-point. At the back of the book is a list of organisations which you may want to contact for further information.

*****

Eating problems

ChildLine information

0800 1111

Many young people experience difficulties with eating and food at some time in their lives. These can range from not liking certain foods (which happens to most people), to serious eating problems which may be medical and/or emotional in origin. 2% of young women and 0.2% of young men are affected by anorexia and bulimia, but about 10% of teenage girls suffer from eating disorders, although some of them have it in a very mild form. In 1994/95, 312 young people spoke to ChildLine counsellors about an eating problem: 304 girls and 8 boys. Of the 250 children who gave their age, 39 were 16 years old, 47 were 15 years old, 58 were 14 years old, and 48 13 years old. Children as young as 10 and 11 also phoned to talk about eating disorders.

What are the most common eating problems?

Anorexia nervosa

People with anorexia nervosa avoid eating and lose a lot of weight. They often feel fat, even when they are very thin. They may use other ways of staying thin, such as taking laxatives (which is dangerous) or exercising too much. They can become very weak and without special help some may even die.

Bulimia nervosa

This is when people binge and then make themselves sick to get rid of the food. People with bulimia may not look overweight or underweight and may find it easy to hide their eating problems. Continuous bingeing and vomiting can eventually do serious damage to the body.

Compulsive eating

This is when people eat much more than their bodies need over a long period, or use food to comfort or distract themselves. This can lead to being overweight and to serious medical problems.

How do eating problems begin?

Eating problems often start as a response to other problems, such as unhappiness in the family, school pressures, the death of someone close, child abuse, or a combination of these and other things.

Without help, the eating problem itself can get out of control. It can damage people's bodies and can leave them feeling bad about themselves and others, depressed and even suicidal.

Many young people deny their eating problem or try to keep it a secret. But the sooner they accept that they have a problem, the easier it is to help. Help can include anything from talking to friends, family or a confidential counsellor such as ChildLine, to seeing a doctor or spending time in hospital.

What do young people tell ChildLine about their eating problems?

- Sarah told a ChildLine counsellor that she started to eat a lot under the pressure of exams. She put on

weight and this led to her being teased and called names. She became very embarrassed about her size and said that one of the things that helped most was to talk to someone who couldn't see her.

- Niri, 15, was doing well at school, had lots of friends and belonged to a drama group; then her family moved to another part of the country. Niri developed anorexia as a way of expressing how very upset she felt about the move.

- Jon phoned ChildLine over many months. He was having medical treatment for bulimia and the whole of his life felt out of control. He told ChildLine that he started bingeing and vomiting after he had been sexually abused. He said 'there is something bad inside me that I need to get out'. Jon said that talking to his ChildLine counsellor helped him to feel more in control of his life and happier about himself.

How can ChildLine help?
- ChildLine counsellors listen without blaming or criticising. They take young people's problems seriously.
- It can be easier to talk on the phone than face to face, especially at first.
- Supportive family and friends are important, but it often helps to talk to someone who is not personally involved.
- Young people can write as well as phone, phone just once, or arrange to speak to the same counsellor over a period of time.
- ChildLine can talk to you about who else can help you with an eating problem.

If you need to talk in confidence about an eating problem, or are worried about someone else with this problem – you can call ChildLine free, 24 hours a day, on 0800 1111, or write to ChildLine, Freepost 1111, London N1 0BR

You can also contact the Eating Disorders Association, First Floor, Wensum House, 103 Prince of Wales Road, Norwich, NR1 1DW.

Suggesting reading:
Eating Your Heart Out, Buckroyd. Published by Optima 1994
Coping With Bulimia, French. Published by Thorsons 1994
Anorexia Nervosa and the Wish to Change, Crisp, Joughin, Halek & Bowyer. Available only from Eating Disorders Association.

© *ChildLine*
January, 1996

What causes eating disorders?

Information from Anorexia Nervosa and Related Eating Disorders, Inc. (ANRED)

There are many theories. For any particular person, some or all of the following factors will be woven together to produce starving, stuffing, and purging.

Biological factors
Temperament seems to be, at least in part, genetically determined. Some personality types (obsessive-compulsive and sensitive-avoidant, for example) are more vulnerable to eating disorders than others.

Also, once a person begins to starve, stuff, or purge, those behaviours in and of themselves can alter brain chemistry and prolong the disorder.

For example, both undereating and overeating can activate brain chemicals that produce feelings of peace and euphoria, thus temporarily dispelling anxiety and depression. In fact some researchers believe that eating-disordered folks may be using food to self-medicate painful feelings and distressing moods.

Psychological factors
People with eating disorders tend to be perfectionistic. They may have unrealistic expectations of themselves and others. In spite of their many achievements, they feel inadequate, defective, and worthless. In addition, they see the world as black and white, no shades of grey.

Everything is either good or bad, a success or a failure, fat or thin.

If fat is bad and thin is good, then thinner is better, and thinnest is best – even if thinnest is sixty-eight pounds in a hospital bed on life support.

Some people with eating disorders use the behaviours to avoid sexuality.

Others use them to try to take control of themselves and their lives.

They are strong, usually winning the power struggles they find themselves in, but inside they feel weak, powerless, victimised, defeated, and resentful.

People with eating disorders often lack a sense of identity. They try to define themselves by manufacturing a socially approved and admired exterior. They have answered the existential question, 'Who am I?' by symbolically saying 'I am, or I am trying to be, thin. Therefore, I matter.'

People with eating disorders often are legitimately angry, but because they seek approval and fear criticism, they do not know how to express their anger in healthy ways. They turn it against themselves by starving or stuffing.

Family factors
Some people with eating disorders say they feel smothered in their families. Others feel abandoned, misunderstood, and alone. Parents who overvalue physical appearance can unwittingly contribute to an eating disorder. So can those who make critical comments, even in jest, about their children's bodies.

These families tend to be over-protective, rigid, and ineffective at solving conflict. Sometimes they are emotionally cold. There are often high expectations of achievement and success. The children learn not to disclose doubts, fears, anxieties, and imperfections. Instead they try to resolve their problems by manipulating weight and food.

Social factors

TV, movies, and magazines are three examples of media that flood people with messages about the 'advantages' of being thin. Impressionable readers and viewers are told, sometimes directly, sometimes indirectly by the actors and models that are chosen for display, that goodness, success, power, approval, popularity, admiration, intelligence, friends, and romantic relationships all require physical beauty in general and thinness in particular.

The corollary is also promoted. People who are not thin and beautiful are represented as failures: bad, morally lax, weak, out of control, stupid, laughable, lonely, disapproved of, and rejected.

Girls and women are disproportionally affected by eating disorders and cultural demands for thinness. Never before in recorded history have females been exhorted to be as thin as is currently fashionable.

Men, by contrast, are encouraged to be strong and powerful. As they work to develop their power in the gym and workplace, they equate 'thin' with 'skinny' and 'weak'. Even though today's female models often look frail, wounded, and vulnerable (characteristics men abhor in themselves), female thinness is not rejected as 'skinny'. Instead it is coveted and defined as glamorous, sexy, and evidence of the with-it woman. Perhaps this explains, at least in part, why only five to ten per cent of people with eating disorders are male.

Triggers

If people are vulnerable to eating disorders, sometimes all it takes to put the ball in motion is a trigger event that they do not know how to handle. A trigger could be something as innocuous as teasing or as devastating as rape or incest.

Triggers often involve the breakup of a valued relationship.

Triggers often happen at times of transition where increased demands are made on people who already are unsure of their ability to meet expectations. Such triggers include starting a new school, beginning a new job, death, divorce, marriage, family problems, graduation into a chaotic, competitive world, and so forth.

Perhaps the most common trigger of disordered eating is dieting. It is a bit simplistic, but nonetheless true, to say that if there were no dieting, there would be no anorexia nervosa. Neither would there be the bulimia that people create when they diet, make themselves hungry, overeat in response to that hunger, and then, panicky about weight gain, vomit or otherwise purge to get rid of the calories.

Feeling guilty and perhaps horrified at what they have done, they swear to 'be good'. That usually means more dieting, which leads to more hunger, and so the cycle repeats again and again. It is axiomatic in eating disorders treatment programmes that the best way to avoid a binge is to never, never allow oneself to become hungry.

Please Note: ANRED information is not a substitute for medical treatment or psychological care. For help with the physical and emotional problems associated with eating and exercise disorders, talk to your physician and a competent mental health pro-fessional.

My teenage diet hell, by Ginger Spice

Ginger Spice Geri Halliwell was not always so keen to show off her voluptuous charms.

The 24-year-old star has revealed how, as a teenager trying to establish herself in show business, she fell victim to eating disorders. It started when she was working as a club dancer, she told the group's office magazine *Spice*, out on Thursday.

'I was about 17 or 18 and I'd never thought about my figure before or questioned the shape I was, but then a couple of the other dancers started commenting I was a bit plump.

'It made me conscious of my weight and I went on a diet. That was the biggest mistake of my life. Diets are a trap. They are the start of a vicious circle that doesn't get you anywhere.'

Geri decided to discuss her teenage problems after young fans of the Spice Girls continually asked about eating disorders.

'They're very hard to understand but problems with food can often be symptoms of your lack of self-esteem, lack of love or the desire to feel a need,' she said. 'Bulimia can be a result of feeling unable to express your hate, love or anger.

'A lot of people don't understand it at all. They think it's easy just to eat your three meals a day but it's not that easy. Quick-fix diets don't work. You always end up the same weight in the end anyway.

'If you're worried about how good you look, I can honestly say that you're just as sexy with a bit of meat on you, as long as you're not hung up about it.'

Anorexia nervosa

Information from the Eating Disorders Association (EDA)

Anorexia nervosa

Anorexia nervosa literally means 'loss of appetite for nervous reasons'. The name itself is misleading because sufferers from anorexia nervosa have not lost their appetite at all. What they have lost is the ability to allow themselves to satisfy their appetite.

It is important to understand that anorexics are not trying to starve themselves to death. On the contrary, anorexia is an attempt to cope with living. It is a solution which is adopted for difficulties which seem impossible to resolve. Anorexia is an expression of conflicts about dependence, autonomy and control, and sufferers are particularly terrified of being out of control. It is because of this fear that food and weight loss assume such importance. This seems to be one area of life which sufferers feel able to control. The anorexic conceals her deep-rooted fear of failure with her success at losing weight. The anorexic attitude towards life combines a very low self-esteem with high expectations and perfectionism. Anorexia is not merely a silly obsession with slimming, or a misguided wish to be slim and beautiful. Rather it is a desperate bid for psychological survival.

Who suffers from anorexia nervosa?

People of all ages may show symptoms of anorexia and cases of sufferers aged from six to sixty have been reported. Although both males and females suffer from anorexia nervosa, it is very much more common amongst women than men. Statistics show that the condition is most commonly found amongst girls, adolescent or slightly older. Sufferers tend to be high achievers who are emotionally dependent on their parents. Although families do not seem to be especially different from average,

anorexia nervosa seems to be more common in families where academic and social achievement tends to be highly valued, but it does occur in all social and ethnic groups.

How common is anorexia?

It is difficult to be certain about the incidence of anorexia nervosa as not all cases are either recognised or treated. However, studies of schoolgirls have shown that between the ages of 16 and 18 about one in every 200 girls suffer from the condition. The incidence is at its highest in the independent sector of education although it is by no means confined to it.

Symptoms of anorexia

The central symptoms of anorexia are weight loss and a great preoccupation with weight. Anorexics are terrified of being or becoming fat. Life for them becomes so dominated by calories, food, and avoiding food that sufferers quickly become secretive and socially isolated. They may become hyperactive and restless, and in women menstruation ceases. Many anorexics suffer the symptoms of starvation: severe constipation, abdominal pain, dizzy spells and swelling, especially of the stomach, face and ankles. A growth of downy hair on the body and loss of hair on the head are not uncommon. The consequences of poor peripheral circulation are often obvious. These include extreme sensitivity to cold and dry, and rough, discoloured skin.

A distorted perception of both self and life can make it difficult for sufferers of anorexia nervosa to accept help. As the underlying emotional difficulties are resolved, however, and a more settled pattern of eating returns, these side effects will usually disappear with time. The human body has remarkable tolerance and can usually return to normal with few or no scars to reflect the past.

The anorexic's perception of herself and her problems

From a distance, anorexics appear to be efficient, decisive and confident. Closer scrutiny reveals that they are fearful that no matter what they do, it will not be good enough.

Anorexics are very concerned with success; they want to be good at everything they do. Unfortunately, no matter how much they succeed, from their point of view it is never enough. In their eyes, other people are always more talented, more intelligent, more attractive. They believe that other people, including their families and friends, share this view. Because they are measuring themselves against a standard which is far beyond what is realistic, they are never happy, and see themselves as failures.

The typical picture of someone who might develop anorexia is of an introverted, conscientious and well-behaved child who has seldom presented problems either at home or school. Many surveys note high intelligence and superior scholastic performance, but the two overwhelmingly consistent personality traits are those of perfectionism and obsessionality. It is when these characteristics are placed within the context of dissatisfaction with life, or when life presents an individual with events for which their existing skills are inadequate, that anorexia becomes a viable alternative.

By concentrating on her fatness (or rather thinness) the anorexic avoids concentrating on herself, her relationships with others, her emotions, and her limitations. Anorexia is only one solution troubled people use as a means of coping with their problems. Some people drink too much, others take drugs, others become more overtly distressed or suicidal. These can all be seen as solutions to issues and difficulties connected with accepting who one actually is, and working out one's own strengths and limitations.

Anorexics and their families

While certain patterns can be found amongst the families who produce an anorexic member, it is important to remember that all families are different and every family, however fortunate, has its own internal problems and times of difficulty. While it would be quite mistaken to assume that families are to blame for anorexia, certain trends have been noticed by researchers which may contribute to the development of anorexia.

People who develop anorexia have often been unusually easy children. They do not answer back and tend to make less fuss and get less angry than their siblings. Looking back on their childhoods, anorexics often say they tried to do what they thought others wanted them to do. They are supposed to be 'good' and 'happy' children, so these were the characteristics they tried to display, whether or not this corresponded to their real feelings.

Most anorexics as teenagers are good students and high achievers. They are anxious to please their parents and teachers. The key word here is 'anxious'. The young anorexic is not just obedient: she worries about her ability to live up to other people's expectations and wishes, and fears that if she fails they will not love, respect or want to know her. Every adolescent and adult shares these fears to some extent, but the anorexic is overwhelmed by them and finds them hard to talk about. She feels that the fears themselves will be ridiculed and will be the cause of her rejection.

Some experts have found the parents of anorexics to be highly demanding. Parents want and expect their children to be successful, but the children may not feel that these expectations are accompanied by enough love or support for themselves as people. The anorexic child often does not know and cannot hear that she is loved as a person. She feels that she is valued for her achievements, but does not feel that her parents really care about her. At some point it all becomes too much and the anorexic feels the need to demonstrate the kind of self-discipline of which she is capable; her own body becomes her greatest achievement.

Other researchers see anorexia as a compromise between equally strong desires for dependence and independence. Many anorexics come from tight-knit families that encourage their children to stay close. The potential anorexic may want to go her own way and prove that she has value outside the family, but at the same time she feels incapable of doing so and wants to be protected and cared for. Unconsciously, she chooses the symptom of anorexia to resolve this dilemma. By her rigid control of her body she is making a clear statement about who is in charge of her life, while at the same time, by becoming ill, she vividly demonstrates how needy and dependent she feels.

Treatment

In order to recover, anorexics must first of all come to accept and begin to like themselves. They must learn gradually to accept their failures and weaknesses and perceive them, together with their strengths, as being the necessary balance for a happy life. This can be a slow process but gradual small changes can be successfully built upon in working towards recovery.

If weight has been allowed to fall to a very low level and the sufferer feels unable to nourish herself at home, a period in hospital may be necessary. Due to a combination of factors – of which inadequate nutrition, environmental stress and emotional confusion make the major contributions – anorexics sometimes become very depressed. In such instances, hospitalisation can be useful as it enables nutrition to be monitored while the home environment is remote and psychotherapy and counselling services are more readily available.

Weight gain alone is not an appropriate goal for treatment. Many anorexics have the experience of gaining weight in hospital only to lose it again when they are discharged. Forcing an anorexic to eat and gain weight may temporarily meet the person's physical needs but will not form the basis of a long-term recovery. Only by treating the underlying problems can the anorexic be helped; emphasis on weight alone will only result in a relapse.

Hospitals vary in the amount of psychological support given. Some offer individual psychotherapy while others use a family therapy approach which aims to involve all family members and see anorexia nervosa as a symptom of family distress. Few hospitals have either the time or the resources to offer psychological help for long if at all. This can be absolutely vital for the recovering anorexic who may find her needs best met by a counselling agency which is not hospital based.

Not all anorexics either need or wish to enter hospital for treatment. Eating Disorders Association has been established as a mutual self-help support organisation which co-ordinates a network of local groups to help both those who suffer alone and those discharged from hospital. Eating Disorders Association is also happy to offer support to the families and friends of those who suffer from anorexia.

• The above information has been kindly provided by Eating Disorders Association (EDA). However, the information is currently in the process of being updated and re-written. The revised leaflets will include the latest information and developments from the field of eating disorders and will be available from EDA from the end of 1998. See page 41 for address details.

Bulimia nervosa

Information from the Eating Disorders Association (EDA)

Bulimia nervosa

Bulimia is a condition in which the sufferer binges – eats exceptionally large amounts of food – and then purges herself by starvation, vomiting, laxatives or diuretics. It is a lifestyle which completely controls the sufferer's every waking hour, an existence in which almost every day, to some extent, is spent thinking about shopping, cooking, bingeing, and finally getting rid of food.

Bulimia usually begins between the ages 15 and 20, although before this time many bulimics will have had problems with eating habits or weight, anorexia nervosa, childhood obesity, adolescent weight in the high-normal range, or lifelong fluctuations in weight. In many cases bulimia begins with the institution of a diet following a distressing event (the break-up of a romance), a challenge (making the gymnastics team), or any situation that encourages the person to think about body shape and its links with control, popularity and achievement. It is probably not coincidental that the peak age of the onset for bulimia, 16 to 18, is a time of transition from high school to college, from the family to independent living.

Sufferers of bulimia nervosa become trapped in a cycle which reinforces their already highly developed feelings of guilt, shame, disgust and self-hatred. They feel great guilt about their bulimia and, while they are often social people to begin with, they are forced into increasingly private lives to avoid the possibility of being found out. This shame and isolation only increase their feelings of inadequacy and unattractiveness.

Because sufferers tend generally to present a public image of self-assurance, happiness and success, bulimia nervosa is a condition which

may go undetected for years. The sad fact is that sufferers are desperately unhappy, have an appallingly low self-esteem and may be exceedingly depressed. Sufferers of bulimia nervosa are usually normal weight, unless the condition has been preceded by anorexia nervosa, and they seem to eat normally when they are with other people.

The causes of bulimia

Much of what has been said about the anorexic and her family is also true of the bulimic. The bulimic is likely to be a good student or employee and desire a high level of achievement, but at the same time has many self-doubts and feels insecure about her ability to handle life's demands and difficulties. She fears she is inadequate and does not have the tools to reach the goals she has set for herself. She believes she does not measure up in looks or accomplishment to other people and may experience problems interacting with them because of her sense of inferiority. She wants to be part of the crowd but fears she will not be accepted.

Stress, anxiety, loneliness, and depression may cause her to eat large quantities of food as a way of releasing the tension. She cannot control her desire for food but she can control whether it remains in her body. Some people turn to alcohol or drugs when they are under stress, upset, or depressed – bulimics turn to food.

Many bulimics fear that once they start eating, they will not be

able to stop. They binge and then purge as a means of giving in to their desire for food and then controlling it.

What is a binge?

A binge is what happens when eating becomes wholly out of control. Enormous quantities of food are consumed in a frenzy – so much so that the food may be eaten uncooked or even straight from the freezer. A binge almost exclusively consists of high calorie foods. These are usually carbohydrates and fats in the form of sweets, chocolate, biscuits, bread, pastry, butter and cheese. There are, of course, many other variations, and food may have been previously selected on a shopping expedition with the binge in mind.

Bulimics loathe the cycle of bingeing and then ridding themselves of food. The purgation, or 'cleansing procedure', is frequently perceived by sufferers as a self-inflicted punishment for the gap which separates their public image from their private selves. The latter, already desolate and stricken by feelings of guilt, comes to be regarded with even great revulsion. Many sufferers have reported that their behaviour, when bingeing, is to them like a hidden side of their personality – a demonic voice which will not release them. They are totally out of control because the 'voice' controls them wholly. So powerful can be the compulsion to binge that there are times when quite literally nothing will prevent sufferers from so doing. As a result, regardless of resolution on the part of sufferers to change, the vicious circle can seem to them to be impossible to break.

If sufferers rely heavily on vomiting to rid themselves of food, then teeth are rapidly affected. The constant acidic action erodes the enamel on the teeth and extensive tooth decay soon follows.

Other dangers associated with bulimia include: ulcers, stomach and bowel disorders, mouth and throat irritations, and gum disease. Loss of hair is common to bulimics as is a general feeling of total apathy after a binge. For those using laxatives or diuretics, there may be serious, even fatal, results. Constant purging and/or vomiting creates severe mineral imbalances in the body as the delicate balance of many mineral salts – absolutely vital for the body to function – becomes deranged. Fatigue or complete exhaustion follow and in the most severe cases stupor, coma and eventually death. This is because the correct balance of mineral salts is vital for the proper functioning of organs such as the heart and kidneys.

Symptoms
Central features
1) Recurrent episodes of un-controllable overeating
2) Efforts to undo the effects of binge-eating by self-induced vomiting, severe caloric restric-tion (abusive dieting), excessive exercising, use of legal or illegal appetite suppressants, and/or use of laxatives or diuretics
3) Chronic anxiety, guilt, depression and tension

Commonly associated characteristics
1) Drastic weight fluctuation
2) Impulsivity and emotional in-stability
3) Acting-out via substance abuse, theft, self-mutilation and/or promiscuity
4) Problems with social adjustment
5) Depression
6) A high need to achieve in order to obtain the approval of others
7) Shop lifting

Bulimics have periods of over-eating which become out of control. These may follow excessively long periods of starvation. The process of starvation leads to cravings for food, which become so strong the sufferer loses control and 'binges'. After a binge a bulimic may resort to laxatives or diuretics, as well as vomiting, to get rid of the effects of bingeing. Many bulimics have a previous history of anorexia nervosa and either 'discover' bulimia nervosa, or turn to bulimia nervosa, believing it will solve their dilemma of wanting to eat whilst remaining thin. Initially, bulimia nervosa may seem to hold the answer for people who are dissatisfied with their lives and dislike what they are. The answer is superficial though and sufferers rapidly find themselves trapped in a dangerous cycle which reinforces self-degradation, guilt and shame. Although some bulimics never experience a real anorexic episode, they nevertheless share the anorexic's abnormal concern about weight and shape, control and lack of control and fundamental need to accept their imperfections as possible strengths. Occasionally there are bulimics whose weight swings from high to low over a period of years – a reminder that anorexia nervosa and bulimia nervosa are not mutually exclusive.

Treatment
As with anorexia nervosa, there is no one way of offering help to bulimics – what suits one woman might not suit another, and anyway not everyone has access to all forms of treatment. One of the greatest difficulties facing women wanting help at present is the sheer lack of resources available.

Bulimic women generally experience extreme ambivalence about giving up the symptom and this is a profound problem for those offering help. In some situations where the sufferer is in a life-threatening condition, or there are other problems involved as well as bulimia, she is admitted to an in-patient hospital programme. But this is not the case for most bulimics.

Unlike anorexics, most bulimics recognise their eating disorder and desperately want help. In another sense however, the bulimic woman's ambivalence about allowing herself to take in anything good can make it difficult to receive help. Self-help programmes or self-help groups combined with back-up counselling support or therapy, and the moti-vation of the bulimic herself, can prove a successful way of tackling this very difficult problem.

Neither anorexia nor bulimia can be cured overnight. Recovery is a long, hard process, which often requires the bulimic to face those painful issues she has been avoiding by being bulimic. She will experience all sorts of difficult feelings – depression, anger, frustration, rage. She may also need help in re-learning about 'normal' eating. The recovered bulimic should also be aware that she needs to develop ways, other than bulimia, of coping with stress.

• The above information provided by Eating Disorders Association is currently in the process of being updated and rewritten. The revised leaflets will include the latest infor-mation and developments from the field of eating disorders and will be available from EDA from the end of 1998. See page 41 for address details.

© Eating Disorders Association
January, 1998

Anorexia – and the disturbing problem no parent can ignore

Ruth Gardner's parents thought she was an ordinary 13-year-old when she first started to lose weight. But over the next three years they watched helplessly as their daughter shrunk to just $3\frac{1}{2}$st. Today, aged 21, Ruth has brought herself back from the brink and weights a relatively healthy $8\frac{1}{2}$st. This article tells her haunting story and offers an in-depth medical insight into a condition that blights so many young lives. Chris Brooke reports.

When Ruth Gardner walked into St James's Hospital in Leeds – made famous by the TV series *Jimmy's* – the sight of her shocked even the most hardened doctors.

She looked more like the survivor of a Nazi concentration camp than a young woman in the prime of her life. Her legs were like matchsticks, her ribs jutted from her chest and her skin limply enveloped her skeletal frame.

In truth, Ruth was lucky to be alive. Through self-deprivation she had pushed the human body to the limit of endurance.

Today, just eight months later, she is unrecognisable as the same woman. She has put on $4\frac{1}{2}$st in weight and her natural, female figure has almost returned. Thanks to her own courage and determination, and the specialist help of the hospital's Eating Disorders Centre, Ruth is on the way to a full recovery.

Ruth's eating problems began almost a decade ago when she was admitted to the prestigious £1,400-a-term Leeds Girls High School, the region's leading private school for girls. At this stage in her education, she was already showing talent in the classroom and on the sports field.

'I was in the volleyball, hockey and swimming teams. Sport was just something I enjoyed,' she recalled yesterday. 'But it was difficult being at an all-girls school because it was so competitive.'

Surrounded by teenagers from wealthy middle-class families, Ruth found it difficult to cope with a culture in which boys and beauty were an obsession.

'Everyone there was so aware of their appearance. I had developed very early and was very conscious about my body. I remember when I was 13 I decided to give up eating food between meals for Lent. But I couldn't stop when Lent ended. Instead of cutting down on eating between meals, I just cut out the meals altogether.'

By the Easter of 1989, Ruth had become a fully-fledged anorexic.

Her parents Michael, 51, a retired teacher, and Helena, 61, a housewife, encouraged her to eat, without success, and had sleepless nights worrying about what to do.

Meanwhile, Ruth's weight obsession took a stranglehold on the life of the whole family.

'I used to weigh myself several times a day after I had something to eat or drink. If I had put on any weight it used to freak me out. It was Mum who first noticed when I started to lose weight and she took me to the doctors.'

With her weight down to 6st she was referred to the York-based Limetrees centre, a specialist unit for adolescents with eating disorders. She was there at regular intervals for three years and long absences from Leeds Girls High added to the stress.

'I felt I was stupid and reduced my eating still further,' she said.

By the time she was 16, and with the help of the Limetrees centre, Ruth was back to her normal weight of 8st. However, crucially, she did not return home to Roundhay, Leeds, to live with her parents. 'I didn't feel I could cope being with them. I shut them out and felt I was better on my own.'

Ruth quit school with no qualifications and tried to start an independent life, moving into a flat on her own. But, forced to fend for herself for the first time, her emotional problems began to overwhelm her.

She tried to commit suicide by taking an overdose and was saved just in time by having her stomach pumped. The next five years were a battle for survival.

By refusing to live with her parents, she found herself either in hospital, being treated for her anorexia, or in foster care.

'My weight went up and down like a yo-yo. I never felt like I was making any progress. Eventually I got to the point when I didn't care if I lived or died.'

It was at this time that Ruth was persuaded to move back in with her parents. But even then, her intake of food was barely enough to keep her alive.

Her typical breakfast consisted of two bran flakes. Lunch was two pieces of bread and a piece of lettuce and her main meal was a small plate of boiled vegetables.

Her weight frequently dropped below 4st and her heart stopped beating on three occasions when she was in hospital care.

In November last year, Ruth was again forced to seek help from St James's Hospital. But because of waiting lists, it wasn't until February this year, that she was admitted to one of the six beds that comprise the specialist unit.

In Ward 36 of Jimmy's Hospital, the area around her bed looks like a typical 21-year-old's bedroom, with posters of the TV sitcom *Friends* on the wall and a clutch of personal photographs of her looking very anorexic beside her bed.

'I still keep the old photos to remind myself of what I looked like. I still can't believe it was me. When I saw one picture it turned my stomach. I was so thin that when I walked, I could hear my heart racing so quickly that I thought I was going to have a heart attack. I used to get upset when people looked at me.'

She has now developed 'quite a taste for chips', weighs a healthier 8st and is looking forward to the future. 'Now I just want to get on with my life and be happy. I feel so much better in myself. People say I have got back my sense of humour and that I'm not talking about food all the time.

'Just trying on clothes will be quite scary. It's frightening if they fit because for years, I've been used to them hanging off me'

'Nobody wants to be anorexic but the thing about this centre is it deals with the underlying reasons why people don't eat.'

She began by eating calcium-rich foods to strengthen her bones and medical staff have now stabilised her condition to such an extent that she is finally nearing her target weight.

'I don't want to say what my target weight is, but I'm on the right road,' says Ruth. She is about to embark on the next stage of her treatment where staff will accompany her to shops and restaurants.

She added: 'It is about being able to cope. The environment in the hospital is very safe but the thought of being in the outside world can be frightening.

'Just trying on clothes will be quite scary. It's frightening if they fit because for years, I've been used to them hanging off me.'

Ruth expects to stay in hospital for another two months, after which she hopes to resume her GCSEs.

'Because of my illness, my education has suffered. I want to go to college but I've got to do it slowly. There is no point in throwing myself

Fact file

- Older women and men can also be victims and children as young as eight have been diagnosed with anorexia.

- Premature death is believed to affect one in ten anorexics – usually from the effects of starvation or by committing suicide.

- It is not just a modern-day phenomenon driven by 20th-century concerns of stress, fashion trends and obsession over body image. The compulsion to starve oneself has been recorded in historical documents for several centuries, with a medical report from 1684 on an 18-year-old girl who was 'like a skeleton clad only with skin'.

- The term anorexia nervosa was coined in 1873, by doctors in London and Paris, who described the symptoms and, tellingly, how no physical cause could be identified.

- At least 70,000 British women aged between 15 and 29 are thought to be sufferers. Contrary to medical thinking a few years ago, it seems to run right through society, cutting across class and income levels.

- As food consumption falls and weight drops, anorexia sufferers start to experience all the medical effects of starvation, which can affect the ovaries, and the ability to have children, the stomach, gut, heart, kidneys, teeth and saliva glands.

- The key to lasting recovery is through psychiatric or psychological help for the sufferer enabling them to deal successfully with the often painful issues the illness allowed her to avoid.

- Cases of anorexia are doubling every decade – but the secrecy and denial surrounding the problem means the numbers could be greater still.

- The Eating Disorders Association has a recorded telephone message about anorexia and bulimia on 0891 615466 (50p a minute).

Jenny Hope

into it to try to get top grades at the expense of eating.

'I know life is not going to be easy but I feel as though I have been given a second chance – and I want to take it.'

Inside the mind of an anorexic

Most of us find it impossible to put off a meal for longer than a few hours. How then do anorexics persistently avoid eating for so long that their body weight falls low enough to endanger their lives?

Psychiatrists believe the explanation lies in the extraordinary personality type usually found in anorexics. These are people whose dedication to the goal of losing weight is pursued relentlessly, to the extent of eating only 200-300 calories a day.

The one in 200 girls between 14 and 18 who become anorexic are, before the illness starts, the kind of child parents dream about – an obedient perfectionist, used to getting good grades at school, often surpassing expectations.

But during adolescence girls usually experience a large spurt in hip growth. It is at this time the perfectionist finds that if she does not watch what she eats, she is in danger of becoming plump and so, she believes, less than perfect.

Her competitive instinct takes over and she decides she will be thinner – and so, once again, better than all around her. Slimness seems to be first prize in the competition of life. As anorexics are used to making sacrifices to get what they want – they stayed in to revise while everyone else was having fun – the pain of hunger signals to them that they must be doing the right thing. At this stage, her doting parents try to get her to eat. While her rebellious friends are annoying their families with unsuitable boyfriends, the anorexic finds the best way to assert her independence is to ignore pleas to gain weight.

Family meals become a battle-ground, where victory is certain for the anorexic because, no matter how much parents cajole, only the anorexic can actually put food in her mouth and swallow.

The obsessional control anor-

exics exert over their weight is driven by a fear of fatness, which to them represents being out of control. This, they believe, leads to failure.

Soon they begin to fear being fat, more than they fear being dead. That is why, for one in ten, the race to be thinnest ends tragically.

• Dr Raj Persaud author of *Staying Sane – How To Make Your Mind Work For You*, published by Metro.

The great medical debate

Doctors have long been divided on the question of the best way to treat an anorexic. While some say sufferers should be allowed to refuse to eat if they want to, others advocate intervention, even force-feeding if necessary.

Dr Robert Lefever, Director of Promis, an addiction treatment centre in London, believes it is a doctor's responsibility to show victims that they can live without anorexia – and the only way to do that is to put them under constant medical supervision.

Some doctors say sufferers should be allowed to refuse to eat if they want to, others advocate intervention, even force-feeding if necessary

---

'Anorexia is the same as other addictive behaviour, such as alcoholism and drugs,' he says. 'Once started, it is difficult to stop.

'An anorexic can be cured, but not as an outpatient. After the sufferer's condition has been stabilised through drip feeding, supervision on a 24-hour basis is then required, preferably with other anorexics.

'The general principle here is to encourage patients to help each other. But if patients refuse help they can be sectioned under the Mental Health Act and forced to take treatment. I would have no hesitation in recommending such drastic action if a life were at risk.'

However, at a conference on medical ethics this year at King's College, London, experts suggested that victims should have the right to starve themselves.

Dr Heather Draper, a lecturer in bio-ethics at the University of Birmingham, argues that doctors are not in a position to decide whether the lives of victims are meaningful or not. It's up to the individual.

She says: 'Undoubtedly it is awful to watch someone die when their lives could be saved – particularly if they are very young. However, if we are to do justice to these sufferers, we must not be deaf to their requests to refuse feeding.

'It is unreasonable to force-feed them if they don't want to eat.'

© *The Daily Mail October, 1997*

How many people have eating and exercise disorders?

Statistics

Anorexia, bulimia, obesity, and binge eating disorder

Research suggests that about one per cent (1%) of female adolescents have anorexia. That means that about one out of every one hundred young women between ten and twenty are starving themselves, perhaps to the point of death.

Research also suggests that about four per cent (4%), or four out of one hundred, college-aged women have bulimia.

Only about five to ten per cent (5-10%) of people with anorexia and bulimia are male. This gender difference may reflect our society's opposite expectations for men and women.

Men are supposed to be strong and powerful. They feel ashamed of skinny bodies. Women, on the other hand, are supposed to be tiny, waif-like, and thin. They diet to lose weight, and if they lose control of the resulting hunger, or develop rigid and compulsive over-control, they can become anorexic, bulimic, or both.

Anorexia and bulimia affect primarily people in their teens and twenties, but clinicians report both disorders in children as young as six and individuals as old as seventy-six.

About one-third (34%) of adult Americans, both male and female, are overweight or obese. Many of these people have binge eating disorder.

Sub-clinical eating disorders

We can only guess at the vast numbers of people who have sub-clinical or threshold eating disorders. They are too much preoccupied with food and weight. Their eating and weight control behaviours are not normal, but they are not disturbed enough to qualify for a formal diagnosis.

Mortality and recovery rates

Without treatment, up to twenty per cent (20%) of people with serious eating disorders die. With treatment, that number falls to two to three per cent (2-3%).

With treatment, about sixty per cent (60%) of people with eating disorders recover. They maintain healthy weight. They eat a varied diet of normal foods and do not choose exclusively low-cal and non-fat items.

They participate in friendships and romantic relationships. They create families and careers. Many say they feel they are stronger people and more insightful about life in general and themselves in particular than they would have been without the disorder.

In spite of treatment, about twenty per cent (20%) of people with eating disorders make only partial recoveries. They remain too much focused on food and weight. They participate only peripherally in friendships and romantic relationships. They may hold jobs but seldom have meaningful careers. Much of each paycheck goes to diet books, laxatives, jazzercise classes, and binge food.

The remaining twenty per cent (20%) do not improve, even with treatment.

They are seen repeatedly in emergency rooms, eating disorders programmes, and mental health clinics. Their quietly desperate lives revolve around food and weight concerns, spiralling down into depression, loneliness, and feelings of help-lessness and hopelessness.

Please note: The study of eating disorders is a relatively new field. We have no good information on the long-term recovery process. We do know that recovery usually takes a long time, perhaps on average five years of slow progress that includes starts, stops, slides backwards, and ultimately movement in the direction of mental and physical health.

If you believe you are in the forty per cent of people who do not recover from eating disorders, give yourself a break. Get into treatment and stay there. Give it all you have. You may surprise yourself and find you are in the sixty per cent after all.

Good statistics are hard to find

Because physicians are not required to report eating disorders to a health agency, and because people with these problems tend to be secretive, denying that they even have a disorder, we have no way of knowing exactly how many people in this country are affected.

We can study small groups of people, determine how many of them are eating disordered, and then extrapolate to the general population. The numbers are usually given as percentages, and they are as close as we can get to an accurate estimate of the total number of people affected by eating disorders.

What about compulsive exercising?

Because anorexia athletica is not a formal diagnosis, it has not been studied as rigorously as the eating disorders. We have no idea how many people exercise compulsively.

Please note: ANRED information is not a substitute for medical treatment or psychological care. For help with the physical and emotional problems associated with eating and exercise disorders, talk to your physician and a competent mental health professional.

© *Anorexia Nervosa and Related Eating Disorders, Inc. (ANRED) 1997*

Helping a friend or relative

Information from the Eating Disorders Association

Why do people get eating disorders?
People often think that eating disorders are just about food and weight. But they are not. They are about feelings as well.

Eating disorders are a way of coping with feelings that are making someone unhappy or depressed. It may be difficult to face up to, and talk about, feelings like anger, sadness, guilt, loss or fear. The eating disorder is an unconscious attempt to avoid these feelings, or to keep them under control. It is a sign that the person needs help in coping with her life and how she sees herself as a person.

There are many reasons why people develop eating disorders. Often there is no one cause, but a whole series of events, feelings or pressures which make the person feel unable to cope. These can include family problems, the death of someone special, problems at school (for example being bullied, or pressure of exams), lack of confidence, or sexual or emotional abuse.

How you can help
What can you do if you think your friend or relative has an eating disorder? You can really help by just being her friend, even when you feel your friendship is being rejected.

What can I do to help my friend?
Give time – and listen. Your friend may just need you to be there when things are hard to cope with. Listen to what she is saying. Try not to give advice, but encourage her to seek help. You should not take responsibility for her illness.

What if she doesn't accept there's a problem?
You may need to accept that your friend is not ready to tackle her eating disorder. But let her know how you

are feeling. Tell her that she can come back to you later. Get some information about eating problems so you can help when your friend is ready to accept that there is a problem.

Should I change my eating habits to fit in with my friend?
No! Don't change your own eating habits. Unless your friend sees a 'normal' amount of food, she could get more and more out of touch with normality. Don't let your friend make you feel guilty about eating a healthy, balanced diet. Try not to talk about food or calories.

How can I stop worrying about my friend?
Don't let the illness ruin your life. Try to enjoy your usual activities, with or without your friend. You can talk in confidence to Eating Disorders Association Youth Helpline if you want some support. (We will ring you back to avoid large telephone bills.) Look after your own needs.

Should I encourage my friend to eat?
No. Everyone needs to decide for themselves what to eat. Your friend is responsible for her own needs.

Why doesn't she join in like she used to?
If your friend has an eating disorder she may find it increasingly hard to join in with social events. She may want to spend more time on her own, and may become more withdrawn and isolated. Tell her why you like her and that you value her friendship. Try to include her in activities. Even if she does not join in, she will still like to be asked. It will make her feel valued as a person, and help with her self-esteem.

Should I tell her parents?
If you find it too difficult to keep it secret, or feel concerned about your friend's safety, then tell an adult you trust. Tell your friend's parents if you really feel they should know. But let your friend know first that you are going to tell someone. You may have

to face the fact that she may not like what you have done, even if you did it for the best, but in time she will probably appreciate your decision.

Will it help if I cover up for my friend?

The best way to help is to let your friend take responsibility for her own behaviour. The problem may go on longer if you cover it up. It would be helpful, though, to suggest that your friend gets professional help. She could discuss this with Eating Disorders Association Youth Helpline, or arrange to see her doctor.

It is very difficult for people with eating disorders to get better on their own. Recovery is much easier with the help and support of those who care for them. It can take a very long time to recover from an eating disorder. Willpower on its own may not be enough.

The sooner your friend or relative gets help, the greater the chance of recovery. But getting better is often a long and painful process. There may be setbacks. Your friend or relative may have mixed feelings about giving up her eating disorder. Part of her may want to change and get better. Another part may feel afraid, and not want to recover. She may see her friends and relatives both as saviours and tormentors. She may see you as a saviour, because she knows you are only trying to help. She may also see you as a tormentor, because she can't cope yet with the pressures of trying to get better.

It is very important to remember that only your friend can take the responsibility for getting better. You can't do it for her. She needs to find different ways of showing her feelings, rather than by controlling what she eats. Only then will she be able to accept that eating is a necessary part of living.

Telephone helplines

01603 621414 – 9am-6.30pm Mon-Fri

Youth helpline (18yrs and under) 01603 765 050 – 4pm-6pm Mon-Fri

Recorded message

If you would like to listen to a recorded message about anorexia and bulimia nervosa call 0891 615466. Calls cost 39p/min cheap rate, 49p/min other times.
Eating Disorders Association
First Floor, Wensum House,
103 Prince of Wales Road,
Norwich, Norfolk NR1 1DW
Telephone:
Admin 01603 619090
Media 01603 624310
Fax 01603 664915

© Eating Disorders Association

Who gets eating disorders?

Gender and age

One study reported that two-thirds of high school students were on diets, although only 20% were actually overweight. Although 90% of reported cases are in women, the rate in men appears to be increasing. Men are more apt to conceal an eating disorder than women so the incidence may be underreported. One recent study of navy men reported a 2.5% prevalence of anorexia, 6.8% of bulimia, and 40% of eating disorders not-otherwise-specified. A study of civilian men with eating disorders reported that 42% of those with bulimia were homosexual or bisexual and 58% of the men with anorexia reported that they were asexual. The other risk factors in men, including depression, personality disorder, and substance abuse, paralleled those in women with eating disorders.

Bulimia has increased at a greater rate than anorexia over the past five years. One study of high school students reported that 2.7% of girls and 1.4% of boys engaged in bulimic behaviour. College-age students are at even higher risks. Estimates of the prevalence of bulimia nervosa among young women range from about 3% to 10%. Some experts claim this problem is grossly underestimated because many people with bulimia are able to conceal their purging and do not become noticeably underweight. Some studies report that 80% of female college students have binged at one time; young people who occasionally force vomiting after eating too much, however, are not considered bulimic, and most of the time this occasional unhealthy behaviour does not continue beyond youth.

Anorexia nervosa is the third most common chronic illness in adolescent women, and is estimated to occur in 0.5% to 3% of all teenagers. It usually occurs in adolescence, although all age groups are affected, including elderly people and children as young as six. Between the mid 1950s and mid 1970s, the incidence of anorexia increased by almost 300%. Indications are, however, that the rate may be stabilising.

Geography and socio-economic factors

Living in economically developed nations on any continent appears to pose more of a risk for eating disorders than belonging to a particular ethnic group; symptoms remain strikingly similar across high-risk countries. Oddly enough, within developed countries there appears to be no difference in risk between the rich and the poor inhabitants. In fact, those in lower economic groups may be at higher risk for bulimia. City living is a risk factor for bulimia but not for anorexia. In one test, people with eating disorders scored significantly higher on IQ tests than those without such disorders. People with bulimia, but not anorexia, had higher non-verbal than verbal scores.

From Eating Disorders: Anorexia and Bulimia, March 1998. Well-Connected.
© Nidus Information Services, Inc., New York NY

Thin end of the Reg

Eating disorders don't just affect women – they can make a misery of men's lives too. Claudia Hammond reports

Mention anorexia or bulimia and most people think of desperate teenage girls, models smoking to stay thin or ballerinas eating tissues to stop the hunger pangs. In other words, eating disorders happen to women. But in fact, as many as one in seven cases involve men.

Jonathan was one of those cases. From the age of five his mother would collect him from school, take him to a bakery and buy him five cream cakes. 'My parents expressed their love through food. My mother colluded with my over-eating – I'd eat an entire tub of ice cream, and she wouldn't ask where it had gone.'

When Jonathan was 17, his eating disorder became more serious. He had reached 28 stone before he visited a university counsellor and began to explore the possible reasons for his bulimia and depression. He put it down to his strained relationship with his parents and to fears of rejection. But there was something else, too – his homosexuality.

It seems that a disproportionate number of men being treated for eating disorders are gay. The idea of having a feminine disorder can deter any man from seeking help and gay men can be more reluctant, fearing their sexuality might be put under the microscope. Researchers in America claimed 90 per cent of men with eating disorders are homosexual but their study, based on a small number, is unlikely to be representative.

Frances Young, a counsellor in Manchester, specialises in eating disorders among men, and found that almost a third of those she sees are gay. Like women, men experience two main eating disorders: anorexia, or self-starvation; and bulimia, which involves bingeing followed by vomiting or the use of laxatives. Some men remain undiagnosed for years. Young finds the slow, creeping nature of the problem can make it harder to spot. 'Men might be picked up for stress or problems at work and then doctors might think they're off their food because of the stress. It's seen very much as a white, middle-class, female problem, and can be missed altogether in men.'

As many as one in seven cases involve men

It's sometimes suggested that anorexia in teenage girls might be connected to a denial of sexual maturity, but very little research has been done to find out why gay men might be susceptible. However, a new study conducted by Iain Williamson, a psychologist at the University of Huddersfield, might shed some light. He gave nearly 100 gay and straight men nine drawings of men ranging from the obese to the emaciated. They had to select the one who most looked like them and the one who would be their ideal. He also questioned them about their dieting behaviour and found that 22 per cent of gay men had very disturbed eating patterns, compared with 4 per cent of the straight men. What's more, the gay men were less satisfied with their bodies and chose a thinner ideal body.

Thinness is equated with attractiveness, particularly in gay culture. A sense of attractiveness is more important to the self-esteem of gay men than straight men. Jonathan, now in his late-twenties, has recovered from his depression and his eating is back to normal. He agrees that there are enormous pressures for gay men to be thin. 'I accept I was over-eating partly to keep myself safe. If I was fat, I couldn't form a relationship with a man. My sexuality wasn't the only thing, but gay men are often more body-conscious than straight men. Everywhere you look in the gay world, there are images of beautiful men.'

Straight women and gay men want to appear attractive to men, but could this desire really cause anorexia? Williamson finds it oversimplistic. 'There's something in it, but it's like saying girls with anorexia want to look like super-models. It makes them seem passive, without looking at the fact that their diet might be the only thing in their life over which they feel they have control.'

Bulimia in gay men could have a different explanation. Very few lesbian women have anorexia, but the incidence of bulimia is similar in lesbian and straight women. Williamson thinks this might suggest bulimia in both gay men and gay women is related to feelings about being gay. 'It's about feeling bad about your homosexuality, partly because of prejudice from other people. So you try to punish your body that's giving you these sexual urges for people of the same sex.' That seems to fit in with Jonathan's experience: 'I felt disgusting being gay and thought I'd never be able to have a normal life. I thought that nobody could love me.'

Of course, most gay men don't have eating disorders, but a minority might be at risk. Young says that for people to get the help they might need, professionals need to look out for eating disorders in both gay and straight men. 'What's important is that practitioners keep their eyes and minds wide open and then they need to listen without making judgments. To be able to understand gay men's needs, they need to have some awareness of gay lifestyles to help them find their own way forward.'

© *The Guardian* September, 1997

Anorexics 'should be allowed to starve'

By Gaby Hinsliff, Medical Reporter

Anorexia victims should have the right to starve themselves to death, an expert on ethics claimed yesterday.

Gaining weight might be as traumatic for victims of eating disorders as radical surgery is for those with terminal cancers, she said.

Even teenagers could make a rational decision to refuse to eat which should in some situations be respected, said lecturer Dr Heather Draper.

'Only individuals can say whether or not their lives are meaningful to them,' she told a conference on medical ethics at King's College, London.

'Undoubtedly it is awful to watch someone – particularly a young someone – die when their lives could be saved.

'However, if we are to do justice to these sufferers who can neither live with anorexia nor live without it, we must not be deaf to their requests to refuse feeding.'

Many anorexics were left 'battle weary' and considered suicide, said Dr Draper, of the University of Birmingham.

'A sufferer accepts that she has a deep-seated problem. But she cannot live with the side-effects that resolving it will bring – namely the body she will be left with.

'Why is this so very different from a sufferer from breast cancer who decides against a mastectomy because her breasts are so important to her identity? We would not override this decision.'

> 'If we are to do justice to these sufferers who can neither live with anorexia nor live without it, we must not be deaf to their requests to refuse feeding'

Her views were criticised by doctors and the anti-euthanasia lobby.

Dr Janet Treasure, who works in the eating disorders unit of London's Bethlehem and Maudsley NHS Trust, said starvation caused biochemical changes in the brain that affected anorexics' ability to make judgments. While they often starved themselves as a protection against deep-seated troubles, that did not make them suicidal. Forced treatment, including feeding, was sometimes necessary.

'In my experience they do not ever really want to die,' she said. 'They can be so confused that they can only see one solution to their problems – not eating. They can't see that they might die.'

Any patient in sound mind has the right by law to refuse treatment, whatever the consequences.

Debate among psychiatrists has focused on whether anorexia is a mental illness that automatically makes sufferers incompetent.

In a recent test case, the High Court ordered an anorexic girl of 16 to be detained – by force if necessary – at a clinic.

Andrew Dunnett of HOPE, an alliance of health professionals opposed to euthanasia, said: 'We would reject any attempt to change medical practice or the law as it stands.

'HOPE remains firmly opposed to the intentional shortening of a patient's life through withholding or withdrawing food and fluids. Such action, whether voluntary or not, is basically euthanasia.'

© The Daily Mail
July, 1997

15

Slim equals beautiful in the minds of most teenagers

Pressure on the young to shape up. By David Derbyshire

Teenagers believe thinness is the most important attribute in the ideal woman, according to a survey.

Waif-like model Kate Moss, *X Files* actress Gillian Anderson and pop singer Louise top the list of attractive women for adolescent boys and girls – almost entirely because they are slim.

By contrast, teenagers believe the ideal male should be smart, muscular and handsome and rate *Eastenders* actor Paul Nicholls, pop star Peter Andre and action hero Arnold Schwarzenegger as perfect men.

The survey reveals the influence that TV and teenage magazines have over young people's attitudes to size and attractiveness. It highlights the pressure now being put on girls and boys as young as 12 to diet – and risk developing eating disorders.

Psychologists at the University of Sussex talked to children between 12 and 16 about what they found attractive in other people and whether they were happy with their own bodies.

Author Dr Helga Dittmar said: 'The key attributes that adolescents link in their descriptions of ideal men are being muscular, handsome and smart.

'In contrast there was only one key attribute used by adolescents to describe ideal women. It was being slim.' The study also reveals that boys are almost as obsessed with their appearance as girls.

Boys who do not bother to 'look good' all too often fall victim to teasing and bullying.

While peer pressure is strong for both sexes, it is brought to bear in different ways for boys and girls.

'Adolescents feel that few girls can look good doing sports, and many can look silly, whereas most boys can look their best by engaging in physical activities,' said Dr Dittmar.

'This has strong implications for girls' and boys' unequal participation on the sports fields.

'For those girls who want to be thin, which is most girls, this restricts their options to dieting, with obvious potentially long-term health implications.'

The psychologists also found that girls are most likely to express unhappiness with their bodies than boys. This is partly an act – an attempt to prove to other girls that they are concerned with how they look –

and partly because boys are reluctant to talk about themselves.

But it is also the result of pressure on girls from boys, who see images of thin, beautiful women in magazines and on television.

The research took place at a mixed-sex comprehensive in a well-to-do small country town in East Sussex. The findings came from interviews and focus groups involving around 70 children.

Dr Dittmar said: 'Extreme forms of eating disorders are well publicised and documented, but we wanted to find out what normal adolescent boys and girls feel about themselves and what particular concerns they have about their appearance.'

The report revealed how youngsters tread a fine line between being teased for wearing unfashionable clothes and being mocked for vanity.

'For boys as well as girls, making an effort with one's appearance is vital,' the report states.

'Adolescents hang round in groups which are held together by a common set of values represented in part by clothes and looks that are passports to admission.

'In order to avoid often severe teasing, adolescents have to display endorsement of these group values.

'This endorsement is emphasised by making an effort with one's appearance. It is the performance of making an effort which is the key to avoiding ostracism.

'Yet there is a fine line, as inappropriate effort may lead to condemnation as vain.'

© *The Daily Mail*
October, 1997

15 diet myths exploded

Eating late at night makes you fat, right? Wrong. Liz Hollis nails the fattest lies about dieting. How many did you believe?

1. Yo-yo dieting wrecks your metabolism and you end up even fatter

The story goes that when you crash diet, regain weight, diet again, your metabolism permanently slows down. Your body thinks it is facing a famine and adapts to survive on fewer calories, so you become much more prone to putting on weight forever afterwards.

The theory sounds persuasive, but it's simply not true. The American National Task Force on the Prevention and Treatment of Obesity examined all the research on yo-yo dieting, and discovered that it has no long-term effect on metabolism. While you're on a diet your metabolic rate may fall, but it will bounce back between two days and two weeks after you start eating normally. The only way to permanently lower your metabolism is to become thinner – a woman who weighs eight stone obviously needs less food to keep her weight stable than a women who weighs 18 stone. But a woman who has dieted to eight stone will have exactly the same metabolic rate as one who has been that weight for 20 years.

2. Eating late at night makes you fat

A favourite one of the diet books. The theory is that you'll convert more of your calories to body fat if you sleep on them, because your metabolism slows down at night and you are less active in the evening. Nice idea, but our bodies are sophisticated machines which can balance out our energy requirements over a week or even a month. 'Frankly, our studies show that it doesn't matter when you eat in a day, it's total calories that count,' says Dr Jebb, a researcher at the Dunn Nutrition Unit in Cambridge. Eating that Mars bar before breakfast is no different to eating it just before you go to bed.

3. Combining certain foods stops your body laying down the fat

Heard the one about never eating protein with carbohydrates? This no-meat – with-potatoes diet is the mainstay of the Hay Diet, which suggests that your body cannot digest both at the same time, because they require different enzymes. The undigested food is stored as fat. 'It may sound convincing but in practice it's gobbledegook,' say Dr Tom Sanders and Peter Bazalgette in their book *You Don't Have to Diet* (Bantam, £5.99). Scientists have also debunked this one.

A Swiss study showed that, when people were given precisely the same number of calories either in three balanced meals or with the protein and carbohydrate separated, body weight remained the same. When people were taught how to combine food and sent home to do it, however, they lost weight. But this was only because cooking became such a complicated, tedious business and meals were so dreary that the 'combination dieters' simply ate less food. And the effect is short-lived – people find that the novelty wears off and they lose motivation. Before long, they're eating meat with their potatoes again.

4. Overweight is caused by a slow metabolism

'For years, overweight people have told their doctors and friends that they eat no more and sometimes even less that their thin friends. They believe they're overweight because of their slow metabolism,' says Dr Susan Jebb. 'However, the slow metabolism theory is a myth. I've tested thousands of overweight people and every single one had a normal metabolism.' The truth is, not only do heavier women have a higher metabolism – they need more calories to stay at their existing weight than a slimmer person – but every single movement take up more energy because they have more weight to move.

5. Grapefruit dissolves fat

You can often tell when somebody is on a crash diet – their supermarket trolley is piled high with grapefruit. Many people believe that the acid in the fruit can destroy fat and stop the body absorbing it This belief was picked up and packaged by the more wacky fringes of the slimming industry which marketed grapefruit pills to help you lose weight. The whole thing is a myth. Grapefruit may have just 22 calories per 100g and be high in vitamin C, potassium and folic acid, but that's as far as it goes. It's also a myth that foods like celery take more calories to digest than they actually contain. But, of course, celery and other very low-calorie foods are helpful in a diet because they fill you and your plate with low-calorie foods.

6. All calories are equal

No, they're not. Fat calories are more likely to be stored than other nutrients and fat calories are particularly fattening. Why? The process of digesting and absorbing food itself burns calories. This is called food-induced thermogenesis, to give it its technical name. It takes more calories to digest protein and carbohydrate than it does fat. For example, 100 calories of protein take 34 calories to digest but 100 calories of fat take only four calories.

7. Drinking lots of water helps you slim

This is a popular myth among dieters. The idea is that drinking loads of water makes you feel full and stops your body absorbing as many calories. 'Some diet gurus even claim that plenty of water will cause fat stores to somehow flow out of the body. Not true. Your body is far too smart to confuse a stomach full of water with a stomach full of food. And water isn't able to do anything to stop you absorbing the calories from that slice of cake you just ate.

8. All fat is bad

Not so. The World Health Organisation says that we need about 30g of fat a day to make sure we get all the nutrients we need. Some vitamins, such as A and D, are also best absorbed when eaten with fat. We also need essential fatty acids from our diet because the body is unable to make them. The fatty oils in fish may help prevent cancer and heart disease. Generally we all tend to eat too much fat. Fatty acid deficiency or deficiencies of fat-soluble vitamins are very rare. Overall, saturated fats increase the risk of heart disease, so replacing them with mono-unsaturated fat may reduce your risk of heart disease and cancer.

9. You can spot-reduce fat

Some diets suggest they can help you spot-reduce fat from your bum, tummy, thighs and hips. Not true. Whatever your method of dieting, weight loss will always follow a similar pattern. You will lose it first from you abdominal cavity, then from your face and between your shoulder blades, and then from hips and thigh.

10. There is a quick way to slim

No. 'If a diet promises rapid weight loss what it means is that you will only end up losing water, which will soon be regained,' says Dr Jebb. You are also more likely to lose muscle

than fat during a rapid weight-loss programme. You mustn't eat less than 1,200 calories a day and aim to lose only one to two pounds a week if you want to make sure you retain the critical value of 75 per cent of weight loss as fat. Fall below this threshold and you are shedding your nice, taut muscles along with the flab.

11. Cellulite fat is caused by toxins – detox and it will disappear.

This is a favourite among beauty therapists who pound your thighs to rid them of 'toxins'.

Ask them exactly what they mean and they may find it difficult to answer. The term 'cellulite' has no medical status. 'Yes, hormones mean that women's thighs may be prone to fat deposits just below the skin,' says Dr Sanders, 'but they are entirely natural'. The lumpiness shows up even more because our skin is thinner than men's. Our thighs aren't storehouses for toxic waste products and junk food doesn't aggravate cellulite by filling your system with toxins.

12 Health foods are slimming

Many people head straight for the health food store then they start a diet. This is not a good idea. Many 'health foods' have more fat and

calories than ordinary food. For example, a muesli bar can be just as bad for you, and contain far more calories, than a bar of chocolate. Many are laden with sugar and contain more than 40 per cent fat. A Picnic bar contains 230 calories whereas a Slim-Fast Fruit and Nut crunch bar has a surprising 385 calories.

13. You should weigh yourself everyday when you're on a diet

Throw away the scales – they are no help at all when you want to get down to a healthy weight. They don't tell you whether you have shed real body fat or lean tissue. Instead, have your body fat percentage measured by a gym instructor. Also, when you start to exercise more, and shed more body fat, you often put on more muscle – which weighs more than fat. Your weight may even go up or not change at all, while your body seems to be looking fitter, leaner and more toned. Instead, use cues like dress sizes and waist and hip measurements.

14. Beauty treatments can help you diet

Don't be fooled. They can make you feel pampered but they can't help banish flabby thighs. You may look slimmer after you've had a beauty body wrap – and you may even measure a few inches smaller around your hips and thighs – but all you've really lost is water.

The inches you've lost will reappear after a couple of days when body fluid is replaced. Instead, book in for a toning gym programme.

15. Diets work for everybody else – it's just me that can't lose weight
With all the dieting success stories paraded by the slimming industry, you could easily believe that diets work for most people. Not so. Although one in five women is on a diet, research shows almost all of them will fail. They may lose weight but it will soon come back with a vengeance. Low-fat eating is the best way to shed excess pounds, but this rarely works for very long. A Canadian study by the Ludwig Institute for Cancer Research showed that most women on low-fat do not keep all their weight off in the long term. This is because dieters compensate by eating more of other foods or they may gradually increase their fat intake again without realising. The only things that work are doing more exercise and making permanent healthy eating changes – and keeping them up forever.

What does work?

- Change to skimmed or semi-skimmed milk.
- Cut out sugar in tea and coffee.
- Grill food instead of frying.
- Eat five portions of fruit and vegetables a day.
- Substitute pickle or mustard for butter in sandwiches. And skip the butter under beans or cheese on toast.
- Exercise regularly. It doesn't have to be a full-on aerobic class – 20 minutes' brisk walking or gardening every day counts too.
- Don't buy biscuits, crisps and cakes – if they're not in the larder, you can't eat them.
- Have at least three alcohol-free days a week.
- Eat until you're satisfied, not until you're full.

Self help – it worked

Vicki's story

My eating disorders began at the age of 18 when I began an unhealthy obsession with dieting. My weight yo-yoed for the next 6 years and for the last 2 years I became bulimic. My family knew about my obsession with dieting but not my bulimia. I kept this a secret. My bulimia was not a daily ritual, it was something I did every now and again when I had overeaten. Sometimes there would be a gap of a couple of months. However, I was never in control of my bulimia – it was in control of me!

As I kept my bulimia a secret I had no-one to talk to. I couldn't see a way out. I had no self-confidence in my appearance whatsoever. Then two years ago I had had enough. My bulimia had got to come to an end. I had to accept and love myself the shape I was. What brought the problem to a head was that I had run myself into the ground – I had filled my life with too many activities (a university degree, part-time work whilst studying and voluntary work) and had worn myself out in the process. I ended up having an emotional breakdown. My family and boyfriend were very supportive.

At the same time I shared a flat with a very close friend who was anorexic. I desperately wanted to help her, but realised that I couldn't because I had to sort out my own problems first.

A week after having my 'breakdown' I had to start my years work experience (2 six month placements in different parts of the country). Moving away actually gave me the opportunity to start addressing my problems. I gave up dieting for good and started exercising regularly. I also realised that I needed to tell my family about my bulimia. Looking back that was the most important thing I did (and the hardest). For the first time

> *It made me think about my own situation and without realising it I looked at the root cause of my bulimia – my obsession with dieting*

in two years – I had faced up to it and admitted that I was bulimic. By being honest with my family and friends and by gaining their support I realised that I had the strength to put my bulimia behind me.

I decided to take a self-help approach using the book *Never Diet Again*. It seemed a daunting task to begin with as there were a million and one questions to answer in the book. By working through the questions it made me think about my own situation and without realising it I looked at the root cause of my bulimia – my obsession with dieting. I believe that this was the key to my success. I had identified the cause and slowly, with my new found confidence, I was able to move onto a bulimia-free life. I can put my hand on my heart and say that I now have no fear of food – I eat what I want, when I want. Because I no longer have forbidden foods, I don't binge.

- The above is an extract from *Signpost*, the newsletter for Eating Disorders Association. See page 41 for address details.

Binge eating disorders

Information from the Weight-control Information Network (WIN)

Binge eating disorder is a newly recognised condition that probably affects millions of Americans. People with binge eating disorder frequently eat large amounts of food while feeling a loss of control over their eating. This disorder is different from binge-purge syndrome (bulimia nervosa) because people with binge eating disorder usually do not purge afterward by vomiting or using laxatives.

How does someone know if he or she has binge eating disorder?

Most of us overeat from time to time, and many people feel they frequently eat more than they should. Eating large amounts of food, however, does not mean that a person has binge eating disorder. Doctors are still debating the best ways to determine if someone has binge eating disorder. But most people with serious binge eating problems have:

- Frequent episodes of eating what others would consider an abnormally large amount of food.
- Frequent feelings of being unable to control what or how much is being eaten.
- Several of these behaviours or feelings:
  1. Eating much more rapidly than usual.
  2. Eating until uncomfortably full.
  3. Eating large amounts of food, even when not physically hungry.
  4. Eating alone out of embarrassment at the quantity of food being eaten.
  5. Feelings of disgust, depression, or guilt after overeating.

Episodes of binge eating also occur in the eating disorder bulimia nervosa. Persons with bulimia, however, regularly purge, fast, or engage in strenuous exercise after an episode of binge eating. Purging means vomiting or using diuretics (water pills) or laxatives in greater-than-recommended doses to avoid gaining weight. Fasting is not eating for at least 24 hours. Strenuous exercise, in this case, is defined as exercising for more than an hour solely to avoid gaining weight after binge eating. Purging, fasting, and strenuous exercise are dangerous ways to attempt weight control.

How common is binge eating disorder, and who is at risk?

Although it has only recently been recognised as a distinct condition, binge eating disorder is probably the most common eating disorder. Most people with binge eating disorder are obese (more than 20 per cent above a healthy body weight), but normal-weight people also can be affected.

Binge eating disorder probably affects 2 per cent of all adults, or about 1 million to 2 million Americans. Among mildly obese people in self-help or commercial weight-loss programmes, 10 to 15 per cent have binge eating disorder. The disorder is even more common in those with severe obesity.

Binge eating disorder is slightly more common in women, with three women affected for every two men. The disorder affects blacks as often as whites; its frequency in other ethnic groups is not yet known. Obese people with binge eating disorder often became overweight at a younger age than those without the disorder. They also may have more frequent episodes of losing and regaining weight (yo-yo dieting).

What causes binge eating disorder?

The causes of binge eating disorder are still unknown. Up to half of all people with binge eating disorder have a history of depression. Whether depression is a cause or effect of binge eating disorder is unclear. It may be unrelated. Many people report that anger, sadness, boredom, anxiety or other negative emotions can trigger a binge episode.

Impulsive behaviour and certain other psychological problems may be more common in people with binge eating disorder.

Dieting's effect on binge eating disorder is also unclear. While findings vary, early research suggests that about half of all people with binge eating disorder had binge episodes before they started to diet. Still, strict dieting may worsen binge eating in some people.

Researchers also are looking into how brain chemicals and metabolism (the way the body burns calories) affect binge eating disorder. These areas of research are still in the early stages.

What are the complications of binge eating disorder?

The major complications of binge eating disorder are the diseases that accompany obesity. These include diabetes, high blood pressure, high cholesterol levels, gallbladder disease, heart disease, and certain types of cancer.

People with binge eating disorder are extremely distressed by their binge eating. Most have tried to control it on their own but have not succeeded for very long. Some people miss work, school, or social activities to binge eat. Obese people with binge eating disorder often feel bad about themselves, are preoccupied with their appearance, and may avoid social gatherings. Most feel ashamed and try to hide their problem. Often they are so successful that close family members and friends don't know they binge eat.

Should people with binge eating disorder try to diet?

People who are not overweight or only mildly obese should probably avoid dieting, since strict dieting may worsen binge eating. However, many people with binge eating disorder are severely obese and have medical problems related to their weight. For these people, losing weight and keeping it off are important treatment goals. Most people with binge eating disorder, whether or not they want to lose weight, may benefit from treatment that addresses their eating behaviour.

What treatment is available for people with binge eating disorder?

Several studies have found that people with binge eating disorder may find it harder than other people to stay in weight-loss treatment. Binge eaters also may be more likely to regain weight quickly. For these reasons, people with the disorder may require treatment that focuses on their binge eating before they try to lose weight.

Even those who are not overweight are frequently distressed by their binge eating and may benefit from treatment.

Several methods are being used to treat binge eating disorder. Cognitive-behavioural therapy teaches patients techniques to monitor and change their eating habits as well as to change the way they respond to difficult situations. Interpersonal psychotherapy helps people to examine their relationships with friends and family and to make changes in problem areas. Treatment with medications such as anti-depressants may be helpful for some individuals. Self-help groups also may be a source of support. Researchers are still trying to determine which method or combination of methods is the most effective in controlling binge eating disorder. The type of treatment that is best for an individual is a matter for discussion between the patient and his or her health care provider.

If you believe you have binge eating disorder, it's important you realise that you are not alone. Most people who have the disorder have tried unsuccessfully to control it on their own. You may want to seek professional treatment.

• The Weight-control Information Network (WIN) is a service of the National Institute of Diabetes and Digestive and Kidney Diseases (NIDDK), part of the National Institutes of Health, under the US Public Health Service. WIN assembles and disseminates to health professionals and the public information on weight control, obesity, and nutritional disorders. WIN responds to requests for information; develops, reviews, and distributes publications to encourage individuals to achieve and maintain a healthy weight. *© Weight-control Information Network (WIN) February 1998*

Compulsive overeating and binge eating disorder

Below are personal definitions of compulsive overeating. All of the following letters were submitted by victims of compulsive overeating or binge eating disorder

Stephanie

I am 24 years old and struggling with compulsive and binge eating for about 15 years now.

It started when I was about 8 or 9 years old, and I struggle with being a compulsive overeater every day and night of my life. My first memory of my disorder was when I was 8. One night after dinner I found myself rummaging through the garbage to finish off what no one else wanted. No one was around. I was very secretive about it. But that was my way of having control in my life.

My parents were always critical of who I was and my body, especially. By no means was I overweight as a child. I had some baby fat, but I guess that wasn't good enough for my parents. As I headed into adolescence, I discovered bulimia and attempts at suicide. My parents took bulimia away from me, so I turned to compulsive overeating. I'd eat in secret, gorging myself with more food than necessary, way beyond the point of feeling full.

Guilt, anxiety and fear would always ensue. Feelings of rage, hatred and loathing would follow; or severe depression with suicidal tendencies. You know it's ironic: I understand my disease enough to know that it all stems from issues of control (feeling out of control and abusing food to regain it). But I am so out of control when I abuse food, that it just becomes a vicious cycle day after day after day. Just to give you an idea of who I am physically, I am 24 years old, 5'3"/5'4" and about 150-155 lbs. Most of my family and friends think I'm about 135-140 lbs. My image of myself is a lot worse than those around me. But anytime any piece of food enters my mouth, I just feel like my body is ballooning out and gaining weight at that moment. I feel as if I physically have gotten bigger just from eating a few bites of food. But that never stops me, though. And it never will until I get the help I need. Scared to continue abusing food and myself, frightened even more not to. It's a terrible trap and addiction and I know there's a way out.

Those of you who see yourself in my story, just remember YOU ARE NOT ALONE!

Tom

I suppose it is ironic that I work at a hospital. I was married to an alcoholic . . . how nice it would be to have a simple addiction like booze . . . you give it up and you are recovering. But you have to eat. Well I eat . . . when I'm hungry . . . when I'm full . . . when I'm anxious . . . when I'm happy . . . when I'm sad . . . well you get the idea. Food, the friend that never fails.

When I was a kid I was trained that food made it all better. When we were totally broke my mom would cook the most. She was a compulsive feeder so I became a compulsive eater.

Every diet has failed. I am a lifer on Weight Watchers, I have been through Nutra System . . . well you get the idea there too. It's not about the weight . . . it is about the inability to deal with feelings and emotions . . . about using a bowl of pasta or a pound of M&Ms as a narcotic to stem the pain.

That is what compulsive overeating is all about.

I cry because it makes me fat and no one sees the real me inside. I try to show the real me and I think that people don't like me because I am fat. Another catch 22 or chicken and egg thing. I see my son getting fat and I grieve. I want out . . . but then I realise that there is no out . . . only control . . . and control is harder than being in or out. Thanks for listening.

Julie

Thank you for listening. My name is Julie. I recently went to the doctor for my weight. The medication that had been on the market had been pulled the week before. I was shocked and still am that she referred me to overeaters. I haven't gone and probably won't. I don't want to label myself that way.

I know I have a problem and have for many years, now that I look back on it. I am 30 years old, 5'3·5" and 212 last checked. I have always enjoyed being active, even if I wasn't good at it. That gave it an extra challenge to get better.

I'm not so much into sweets but starchy food, soothing food I call it.

Mashed potatoes, not a lot of salt or butter (margarine), no sour cream, macaroni and cheese, bread. They have good mouth feel. At night I sneak, I hate coming back to bed, creaking the door open and shut. The shame that my husband knows what I have done. It's not every night, I'm not sure what triggers it.

I am terribly lonely and have been for so long. It feels like I am being swallowed up in isolation. There seems no way out so I sleep a lot to keep from eating.

I have been praying and going to a wonderful Bible class. Attend church regularly. All these places are so structured there seems no time for socialising. I love to go to school with the kids. Why do adults have to be so isolated? Where do you go to find friends in this world anyway? We live in the country. I have people I know and they know me and our family but we never go to each other's homes.

I have got off the subject. My mother has a weight problem. My aunt has a very big weight problem. Part of it is heredity.

I do so much better when I have a routine in MY life. Essential is prayer, Bible reading and keeping close with the Lord. It is so peaceful when we are close to him. It does take some work and watching and listening to get there but it's a wonderful balancer. He accepts us the way we are. He wants to be with us. If you listen quietly you can hear him gently encouraging you and showing your mistakes without it hurting so bad. Slowly and willing you will start to change habits and accepting the changes you need to make. Your heart will soften. Try it consistently, listen to a Christian radio station that has your kind of music (there are varieties, you may be surprised!) Read the Bible in the quiet times of the day. Search the Internet for questions you have about the Bible.

Exercise also is a big help. Getting outside to take a five-minute walk does wonders. There is something to live for, it is being created right now and will be waiting for you if you believe. You can believe it because look what he has done all around us already.

Athletes and eating disorders

Eating disorders continue to be on the rise among athletes, especially those involved in sports that place great emphasis on the athlete to be thin. Sports such as gymnastics, figure skating, dancing and synchronised swimming have a higher percentage of athletes with eating disorders, than sports such as basketball, skiing and volleyball.

According to a 1992 American College of Sports Medicine study, eating disorders affected 62 per cent of females in sports like figure skating and gymnastics. Famous gymnasts Kathy Johnson, Nadia Comaneci and Cathy Rigby have come forward and admitted to fighting eating disorders. Cathy Rigby, a 1972 Olympian, battled anorexia and bulimia for 12 years. She went into cardiac arrest on two occasions as a result of it.

Many female athletes fall victim to eating disorders in a desperate attempt to be thin in order to please coaches and judges. Many coaches are guilty of pressuring these athletes to be thin by criticising them or making reference to their weight. Those comments could cause an athlete to resort to dangerous methods of weight control and can do serious emotional damage to the athlete.

In sports where the athletes are judged by technical and artistic merit, they are under enormous pressure to be thin, because many of the judges consider thinness to be an important factor when deciding the artistic score. In 1988, at a meet in Budapest, a US judge told Christy Henrich, one of the world's top gymnasts, that she was too fat and needed to lose weight if she hoped to make the Olympic squad. Christy resorted to anorexia and bulimia as a way to control her weight, and her eating disorders eventually took her life. At one point her weight had plummeted as low as 47 lbs. On July 26, 1994, at the age of 22, Christy Henrich died of multiple organ failure.

> ### Athletes need to be assured that they will not be criticised or looked down on if they do come forward with their problem

---

Athletes with eating disorders can be at a higher risk for medical complications such as electrolyte imbalances and cardiac arrhythmias.

They are already engaging in strenuous physical activity and putting a lot of pressure on the body. Having an eating disorder puts them at great risk of sudden death from cardiac arrest. It is usually difficult to convince athletes that they are in need of help because they usually believe that they will become a better athlete, and perform better, if they lose more weight. Gymnastics is one sport where the size of the gymnast has changed drastically over the years. In 1976 the average gymnast was 5'3" weighing 105 lbs, and in 1992 the average gymnast was 4'9" weighing 88 lbs.

Coaches and trainers really need to educate themselves on the dangers and on the signs to look for in an athlete that may be suffering from an eating disorder. They must be able to recognise when healthy training routines turn into an obsession where the athlete turns to drastic measures to become thin and succeed in their sport. Coaches should also bring in nutrition experts to educate the athletes on healthy eating and to make them aware of how important it is to eat properly, especially when involved in such intense training. Counselling should also be made available to athletes that are suffering from eating disorders and they should be encouraged and supported to accept the help available to them.

They need to be assured that they will not be criticised or looked down on if they do come forward with their problem.

For parents that are putting their child into a competitive sport, I would recommend that you accompany your child to some training sessions, especially in the beginning, so that you can observe the coach and his methods of training. You do not want your child to be trained by someone who is going to put too much pressure on the athlete to succeed. You want someone that will encourage and help the athlete to develop a healthy routine that will not put them at risk of harming themselves.

You also want a coach that will praise the athlete and be proud of them no matter what place they finish in a competition. The coaches should only expect the athletes to do their best, they should not be expected to be number one. Resorting to dangerous methods of weight control to try and succeed and win competitions is only putting your life in great danger. No gold medal is worth dying for.

Obesity

Information from Anorexia Nervosa and Related Eating Disorders, Inc. (ANRED)

Like most things, obesity is a complex phenomenon about which it is dangerous to generalise. What is true for one person is not necessarily true for the next. Nevertheless, we shall try to make sense out of conflicting theories and give answers to people who struggle to maintain self-esteem in a world that seems to be obsessed with youth, thinness, and the perfect body – whatever that may be.

What is obesity?

A person with anorexia nervosa may define obesity as a weight gain of five pounds, from 89 to 94. A grandmother past menopause may call herself obese because she carries 165 pounds on her large-boned, muscular body. A modelling agency may talk about obesity when one of the women on the payroll puts 135 pounds on her 5'10" body.

None of these women is clinically obese. The anorexic and the model are underweight.

Men are split in their personal definitions of obesity. Many are just as concerned about overweight as women are, while others, frankly rotund, believe they are just fine, perfectly healthy, and universally attractive to potential romantic partners.

Many physicians consider a person to be obese only if s/he weighs more than 20% above expected weight for age, height, and body build. Morbid or malignant obesity is usually considered to be any weight in excess of 100 pounds above that expected for age, height, and build.

In recent years, the definition of expected, or healthy, weight has expanded to include more pounds per height in view of research that links reduced mortality (longer lives)
with more weight than is currently considered fashionable.

What are the causes of obesity?

- Consumption of more calories than are burned through work, exercise, and other activities.
- Inexpensive, tasty, plentiful food and a combination of leisure time, sedentary lifestyle, TV, and other 'activities' that require little or no physical activity.
- Attempts to medicate or escape emotional pain and distress. For various emotional reasons, including loneliness and depression, some people eat when their bodies do not need food.
- Diets and prolonged caloric restriction. When people try to make the body thinner than it is genetically programmed to be, it retaliates by becoming ravenous and vulnerable to binge eating. Ninety-eight per cent of dieters regain all the weight they manage to lose, plus about 10 extra pounds, within five years. Yo-yo dieting repeats the cycle of weight loss followed by ever-increasing weight gain when hunger

ultimately wins.
- Some individuals are obese because of specific biological problems such as malfunctioning thyroid or pituitary glands. Others may have physical problems or disabilities that severely limit or prohibit entirely exercise, strenuous work, and other physical activity.
- Researchers believe that in most cases obesity represents a complex relationship between genetic, psychological, physiological, metabolic, socio-economic, and cultural factors.

The children of heavy parents are more likely to be heavy than the children of thin parents. If friends and family members offer comfort in the form of food, people will learn to deal with painful feelings by eating instead of using more effective strategies. Poor folks tend to be fatter than the affluent. People living in groups that frequently celebrate and socialise at get-togethers featuring tempting food tend to be fatter than those who do not. Some individuals eat great quantities of food, exercise moderately or not at all, and never seem to gain weight. Others walk past a bakery and gain ten pounds. No two people are the same, and no two obesity profiles are identical.

Health risks associated with obesity

- Hypertension (high blood pressure, a contributor to stroke and heart disease). Overweight young people (20-45) have a six times higher incidence of hypertension than do peers who are normal weight. Older obese folks seem to be at even greater risk.
- Diabetes. Even moderate obesity, especially when the extra fat is carried in the stomach and abdomen (instead of hips and thighs), increases the risk of non-insulin dependent diabetes mellitus (NIDDM) tenfold.
- Cardiovascular disease. Both the degree of obesity and the location of fat deposits contribute to the potential for heart and blood vessel disease. The fatter the person, the higher the risk. People who carry extra weight in the trunk area (stomach and abdomen) are at higher risk than folks who store fat in hip and thigh deposits.
- Cancer. Obese men are at elevated risk of developing cancer of the colon, rectum, and prostate. Obese women are at elevated risk of developing cancer of the breast, cervix, uterus, and ovaries.
- Endocrine problems. Irregular menstrual cycles; other menstrual problems; and pregnancy complications, especially toxemia and hypertension. Hormone imbalances of various kinds may contribute to, or be the result of, obesity.
- Gall bladder disease. Obese women 20-30 years old are at six times greater risk of gall bladder disease than their normal-weight peers. By age 60 almost one-third of obese women will have developed gall bladder disease.
- Lung and breathing problems. Obesity can impede the muscles that inflate and ventilate the lungs. Obese individuals may have to work hard to get enough air and over time may not be able to take in the oxygen needed by all body cells.

- Arthritis. Obese individuals are at increased risk of developing gouty arthritis, a distressingly painful disorder. Excess weight stresses vulnerable joints, in particular the back and knee, which may develop osteoarthritis, a mechanical rather than metabolic problem.

Other problems associated with obesity

- Sleep disturbances including sleep apnea (breathing stops for several seconds; then the person rouses, gasps, and struggles to catch breath; episodes may continue through the night)
- Inability to fully participate in recreational activities
- Inability to compete effectively in sports and athletics; being picked last, or not at all, for team sports
- Inability to perform some jobs; reduced job opportunities
- Prejudice and discrimination in school and the workplace
- Restricted social opportunities
- Restricted opportunities for romantic relationships
- Low self-esteem and body-image problems, related at least in part to prejudice and discrimination encountered in school, at work, and in social settings.

One important piece of good news

Obese people do not seem to have any more psychological problems, or more serious psychological problems, than folks of normal weight. The problems they do have are more likely a consequence of prejudice and discrimination than a cause of overweight. In fact, several studies have suggested that the obese are significantly less anxious and depressed than normal-weight peers.

What can be done about obesity?

The simplistic answer: eat less and exercise more.

The realistic answer:
- Work with a physician to identify and correct any underlying medical, biological, or physiological problems contributing to excess weight.

- Check with a counsellor to see if you are using food for a purpose food cannot fulfil: love, comfort, escape, an antidote to boredom, and so forth. If you are self-medicating with food, work with the therapist to come up with better ways of managing stress, painful emotions, and problems.
- Don't ever diet or restrict calories when you are legitimately hungry. If you do, you will set yourself up to binge later.
- Eat normal, reasonable, moderate amounts of healthy foods. Emphasise fruits, vegetables, and whole grains. Don't cut out sweets and fats completely. If you do, you will crave and sneak them. Besides, your body needs the nutrients found in fats and carbohydrates. Just don't overdo it.
- Most important: exercise consistently. Get regular amounts of moderate, self-loving exercise. Start with a few minutes of walking and slowly extend the time until you can do 30-60 minutes a day, 3-5 days a week.
- If you haven't exercised in a while, be sure to check with your doctor first.
- Find a support system. Friends are great; so are support groups. There are both online and in-person opportunities.
- Be gentle and realistic with yourself. If everyone in your family is round and sturdy, chances are you will never be a super model – but you can be happy and healthy. Also remember that healthy, realistic weight loss takes time. Losing one-half to one pound a week isn't very glamorous, but if you go any faster, you will make yourself hungry, and hunger will inevitably make you overeat.

What about taking pills and other medications to lose weight?

- Over-the-counter products. There are many items in drugstores and health food stores that claim to help people lose weight. None seem to be both safe and effective. The ones that are

It's not how fat a fellow is, it's where he's fat

Nutrition experts should be looking at the waist, not the weight.
By Jenny Hope, Medical Correspondent

The wrong people have been targeted for help with their weight problems, says a nutrition expert.

It is not so important how fat you are as where the fat is, according to Dr Margaret Ashwell, former science director of the British Nutrition Foundation.

There is growing concern about obesity, which is linked to cancer, stroke, heart disease, high blood pressure and diabetes. But Dr Ashwell says that not all obesity is dangerous and the distribution of fat is the most important factor.

She believes that men have a bigger weight problem than official statistics reveal because their fat tends to be round the waist. Fewer women face the same dangers because their fat is carried around the hips. As a result, the standard way of measuring obesity is missing men who are at serious risk of heart disease and premature death.

The same system might have wrongly classified one woman in four as being so overweight she could face an early grave.

'There is overwhelming evidence that the health risks of obesity are related more to fat inside the abdomen than total body fat,' said Dr Ashwell.

'The classic pear-shaped figure in which women carry extra weight around their bottom, hips and thighs compared with their waist is a healthy shape.

'Most men who put on weight tend to carry it around their tummies, in an apple shape, and this is the most dangerous area for fat distribution.'

An example of the shape was comic actor Oliver Hardy, who was 6ft 2in and 22stone.

The ratio between waist and height measurements provides a much more accurate predictor of an individual's chances of dying young or from a heart attack than traditional weight-to-height measurements, Dr Ashwell said.

> **'There is overwhelming evidence that the health risks of obesity are related more to fat inside the abdomen than total body fat'**

Research involving 7,000 middle-aged men and women found a direct link between the ratio of their waist and height measurements and their deaths from all causes, particularly heart disease. The greater the waist measurement in relation to height, the higher the health risk.

The new approach would reverse current obesity fears in Britain, where statistics show 17 per cent of women and 13 per cent of men are so overweight it endangers their health.

Using waist-to-height measurements, a lower proportion of women are at risk, 13 per cent, compared with 17 per cent of men.

Dr Ashwell, who now runs an independent scientific consultancy in Ashwell in Hertfordshire, has developed a chart which will be presented in November at a medical conference in Mexico.

The Ashwell Shape Chart, which has been put under copyright, gives four risk categories; Underweight, OK, Take Care and Action. Those in the Action category have the highest chance of premature death.

© *The Daily Mail*
September, 1997

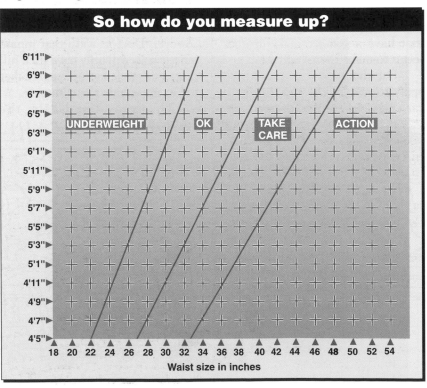

So how do you measure up?

UNDERWEIGHT OK TAKE CARE ACTION

Waist size in inches

Physical activity and weight control

Information from the Weight-control Information Network (WIN)

Regular physical activity is an important part of effective weight loss and weight maintenance. It also can help prevent several diseases and improve your overall health. It does not matter what type of physical activity you perform – sports, planned exercise, household chores, yard work, or work-related tasks – all are beneficial. Studies show that even the most inactive people can gain significant health benefits if they accumulate 30 minutes or more of physical activity per day. Based on these findings, the US Public Health Service has identified increased physical activity as a priority in Healthy People 2000, our national objectives to improve the health of Americans by the year 2000.

Research consistently shows that regular physical activity, combined with healthy eating habits, is the most efficient and healthful way to control your weight. Whether you are trying to lose weight or maintain it, you should understand the important role of physical activity and include it in your lifestyle.

How can physical activity help control my weight?

Physical activity helps to control your weight by using excess calories that otherwise would be stored as fat. Your body weight is regulated by the number of calories you eat and use each day. Everything you eat contains calories, and everything you do uses calories, including sleeping, breathing, and digesting food. Any physical activity in addition to what you normally do will use extra calories.

Any type of physical activity you choose to do – strenuous activities such as running or aerobic dancing or moderate-intensity activities such as walking or household work – will increase the number of calories your body uses. The key to successful weight control and improved overall health is making physical activity a part of your daily routine.

What are the health benefits of physical activity?

In addition to helping to control your weight, research shows that regular physical activity can reduce your risk of several diseases and conditions and improve your overall quality of life. Regular physical activity can help protect you from the following health problems.

Heart disease and stroke

Daily physical activity can help prevent heart disease and stroke by strengthening your heart muscle, lowering your blood pressure, raising your high-density lipoprotein (HDL) levels (good cholesterol) and lowering low-density lipoprotein (LDL) levels (bad cholesterol), improving blood flow, and increasing your heart's working capacity.

High blood pressure

Regular physical activity can reduce blood pressure in those with high blood pressure levels. Physical activity also reduces body fatness, which is associated with high blood pressure.

Noninsulin-dependent diabetes

By reducing body fatness, physical activity can help to prevent and control this type of diabetes.

Obesity

Physical activity helps to reduce body fat by building or preserving muscle mass and improving the body's ability to use calories.

Balancing the calories

Balancing the calories you use through physical activity with the calories you eat will help you achieve your desired weight. When you eat more calories than you need to perform your day's activities, your body stores the extra calories and you gain weight. When you eat fewer calories than you use, your body uses the stored calories and you lose weight. When you eat the same amount of calories as your body uses, your weight stays the same.

Calories in food > calories used =
WEIGHT GAIN

Calories in food < calories used =
WEIGHT LOSS

Calories in food = calories used =
WEIGHT STAYS THE SAME

Source: Weight-control Information Network (WIN)

When physical activity is combined with proper nutrition, it can help control weight and prevent obesity, a major risk factor for many diseases.

Back pain

By increasing muscle strength and endurance and improving flexibility and posture, regular exercise helps to prevent back pain.

Osteoporosis

Regular weight-bearing exercise promotes bone formation and may prevent many forms of bone loss associated with ageing.

Studies on the psychological effects of exercise have found that regular physical activity can improve your mood and the way you feel about yourself. Researchers also have found that exercise is likely to reduce depression and anxiety and help you to better manage stress.

Keep these health benefits in mind when deciding whether or not to exercise. And remember, any amount of physical activity you do is better than none at all.

How much should I exercise?

For the greatest overall health benefits, experts recommend that you do 20 to 30 minutes of aerobic activity three or more times a week and some type of muscle strengthening activity and stretching at least twice a week. However, if you are unable to do this level of activity, you can gain substantial health benefits by accumulating 30 minutes or more of moderate-intensity physical activity a day, at least five times a week.

If you have been inactive for a while, you may want to start with less strenuous activities such as walking or swimming at a comfortable pace.

Beginning at a slow pace will allow you to become physically fit without straining your body. Once you are in better shape, you can gradually do more strenuous activity.

Moderate-intensity activity

Moderate-intensity activities include some of the things you may already be doing during a day or week, such as gardening and housework. These activities can be done in short spurts – 10 minutes here, 8 minutes there.

Heart rate zones

To get the most health benefits from aerobic activity, you should exercise at a level strenuous enough to raise your heart rate to your target zone. Your target heart rate zone is 50 to 75 per cent of your maximum heart rate.

Age	Target Heart Rate Zone 50-75%	Average Maximum Heart Rate 100%
20-30 years	98-146 beats per min.	195
31-40 years	93-138 beats per min.	185
41-50 years	88-131 beats per min.	175
51-60 years	83-123 beats per min.	165
61+ years	78-116 beats per min.	155

Source: Weight-control Information Network

Alone, each action does not have a great effect on your health, but regularly accumulating 30 minutes of activity over the course of the day can result in substantial health benefits.

To become more active throughout your day, take advantage of any chance to get up and move around. Here are some examples:

- Take a short walk around the block
- Rake leaves
- Play actively with the kids
- Walk up the stairs instead of taking the elevator
- Mow the lawn
- Take an activity break – get up and stretch or walk around
- Park your car a little farther away from your destination and walk the extra distance

The point is not to make physical activity an unwelcome chore, but to make the most of the opportunities you have to be active.

Aerobic activity

Aerobic activity is an important addition to moderate-intensity exercise. Aerobic exercise is any extended activity that makes you breathe hard while using the large muscle groups at a regular, even pace. Aerobic activities help make your heart stronger and more efficient. They also use more calories than other activities. Some examples of aerobic activities include:

- Brisk walking
- Jogging
- Bicycling
- Swimming
- Aerobic dancing

- Racket sports
- Rowing
- Ice or roller skating
- Cross-country or downhill skiing
- Using aerobic equipment (i.e., treadmill, stationary bike)

To get the most health benefits from aerobic activity, you should exercise at a level strenuous enough to raise your heart rate to your target zone. Your target heart rate zone is 50 to 75 per cent of your maximum heart rate (the fastest your heart can beat). To find your target zone, look for the category closest to your age in the chart above and read across the line. For example, if you are 35 years old, your target heart rate zone is 93-138 beats per minute.

To see if you are exercising within your target heart rate zone, count the number of pulse beats at your wrist or neck for 15 seconds, then multiply by four to get the beats per minute. Your heart should be beating within your target heart rate zone. If your heart is beating faster than your target heart rate, you are exercising too hard and should slow down. If your heart is beating slower than your target heart rate, you should exercise a little harder.

When you begin your exercise programme, aim for the lower part of your target zone (50 per cent). As you get into better shape, slowly build up to the higher part of your target zone (75 per cent). If exercising within your target zone seems too hard, exercise at a pace that is comfortable for you. You will find that, with time, you will feel more comfortable exercising and can slowly increase to your target zone.

Stretching and muscle strengthening exercises

Stretching and strengthening exercises such as weight training should also be a part of your physical activity programme. In addition to using calories, these exercises strengthen your muscles and bones and help prevent injury.

Tips to a safe and successful physical activity programme

Make sure you are in good health. Answer the following questions* before you begin exercising.

1. Has a doctor ever said you have heart problems?
2. Do you frequently suffer from chest pains?
3. Do you often feel faint or have dizzy spells?
4. Has a doctor ever said you have high blood pressure?
5. Has a doctor ever told you that you have a bone or joint problem, such as arthritis, that has been or could be aggravated by exercise?
6. Are you over the age of 65 and not accustomed to exercise?
7. Are you taking prescription medications, such as those for high blood pressure?
8. Is there a good medical reason, not mentioned here, why you should not exercise?

*Source: British Columbia Department of Health

If you answered 'yes' to any of these questions, you should see your doctor before you begin an exercise programme.

- Follow a gradual approach to exercise to get the most benefits with the fewest risks. If you have not been exercising, start at a slow pace and as you become more fit, gradually increase the amount of time and the pace of your activity.
- Choose activities that you enjoy and that fit your personality. For example, if you like team sports or group activities, choose things such as soccer or aerobics. If you prefer individual activities, choose things such as swimming or walking. Also, plan your activities for a time of day that suits your personality. If you are a morning person, exercise before you begin the rest of your day's activities. If you have more energy in the evening, plan activities that can be done at the end of the day. You will be more likely to stick to a physical activity programme if it is convenient and enjoyable.
- Exercise regularly. To gain the most health benefits it is important to exercise as regularly as possible. Make sure you choose activities that will fit into your schedule.
- Exercise at a comfortable pace. For example, while jogging or walking briskly you should be able to hold a conversation. If you do not feel normal again within 10 minutes following exercise, you are exercising too hard. Also, if you have difficulty breathing or feel faint or weak during or after exercise, you are exercising too hard.
- Maximise your safety and comfort. Wear shoes that fit and clothes that move with you, and always exercise in a safe location. Many people walk in indoor shopping malls for exercise. Malls are climate-controlled and offer protection from bad weather.
- Vary your activities. Choose a variety of activities so you don't get bored with any one thing.
- Encourage your family or friends to support you and join you in your activity. If you have children, it is best to build healthy habits when they are young. When parents are active, children are more likely to be active and stay active for the rest of their lives.
- Challenge yourself. Set short-term as well as long-term goals and celebrate every success, no matter how small.

Whether your goal is to control your weight or just to feel healthier, becoming physically active is a step in the right direction. Take advantage of the health benefits that regular exercise can offer and make physical activity a part of your lifestyle.

© Weight-control Information Network (WIN) February, 1998

Meat eaters are more likely to be obese

People who eat meat regularly have a greater chance of becoming obese than people who have a meat-free diet, according to Imperial Cancer Research Fund scientists.

Their findings are published today in a letter to the *British Medical Journal* and refer to a survey of over 21,000 men and women who were monitored for obesity as part of the Europe-wide EPIC study into cancer and diet. People taking part in the study were categorised as being meat eaters, fish eaters, vegetarians or vegans.

Within the group of meat eaters 9.2 per cent of women and 6.4 per cent of men were clinically obese (people who are approximately 20 per cent over their ideal weight). These figures are higher than the Government's Health of the Nation targets for reducing obesity in England to 8 per cent for women and 6 per cent for men by the year 2005.

One of the researchers for the study, Dr Tim Key of the Imperial Cancer Research Fund's Cancer Epidemiology Unit in Oxford, said: 'The people in this study were recruited through vegetarian and health food societies, shops and magazines and probably lead a relatively health-conscious lifestyle. The prevalence of obesity was low compared with recent national figures, which were 16 per cent for women and just over 13 per cent for men, but the people who ate meat still failed to reach the Health of the Nation targets for obesity. In contrast, the prevalence of obesity was lower in people who did not eat meat.

'Obesity is an increasing problem in Britain and can be caused by eating many different types of food. It causes a lot of ill health, including a large increase in the risk for cancer of the womb and a moderate increase in the risk for breast cancer in post-menopausal women.'

© Imperial Cancer Research Fund

The real reason so many of us are overweight

Obesity threatens the lives of one in five Britons. By Oliver James

We are fast becoming a nation of fatties. According to the World Health Organisation (WHO), about one in five people in Britain is obese, while many more are overweight.

It seems strange in a country so obsessed with dieting, working out and eating healthily that there are so many fat people. And their numbers are growing: the WHO found that only about one in 14 was obese less than two decades ago.

But what seems even stranger, as airlines are forced to enlarge their seats and clothes manufacturers tailor their products to the expanding girths, is how few people are prepared to state the obvious.

The reason that so many people are so overweight is simple: they are eating far too much, and exercising far too little. We have become a nation of gluttons.

Gluttony is, of course, one of the seven deadly sins, so it is no surprise that today even the word has a rather old-fashioned feel to it. But the solution, surely, is for all those people worried about their bulges just to say No.

To state such an obvious fact is, today, almost heresy. Fat is now not only a feminist issue, it has become a bastion of political correctness. I can almost hear Ms Dawn French accusing me of being fattist, cruelly passing judgment on someone's appearance when they can do little about it.

Massive

So it is time to point out some alarmingly obvious facts, ignored both by the mealy-mouthed and those whose mouths are either full of junk food or just talking junk.

My concern at seeing so many massive bottoms wobbling down the street is not that I want to mock my fatter fellow citizens. They face increased dangers of heart failure, strokes, back trouble, arthritis and some cancers, so I am merely pointing out a serious medical problem.

These afflictions needlessly cost the NHS massive sums of money each year, leaving aside the £30 million spent annually treating obesity.

The reason that so many people are so overweight is simple: they are eating far too much, and exercising far too little

---

I have often heard people claim that their bulging paunch or tree-trunk thighs are the result of a heavy bone structure or a slow metabolism – 'it's in the family'. So how come the proportion of obese Britons has increased so rapidly when it takes centuries for our genes to change?

There is little doubt from scientific studies that in the vast majority of cases, how fat we are is the direct consequence of how many calories we ingest.

This is a wholly new problem in the history of the world. We have beaten one of the most enduring challenges to human life – starvation. Yet our triumph has become a threat to our health.

So why do so many of us eat too much? Firstly, it must be said in our defence that there is more temptation than ever before. Modern technology has been stunningly successful in creating diversity and abundance. Unfortunately, like all animals, humans were designed to assume that the supply is scarce and not that there would be unlimited, highly calorific food.

Furthermore, back in the primordial swamp, we took plenty of exercise, whether escaping the jaws of sabre-toothed tigers or trying to ensnare mammoths. By contrast today, the nearest we may get to breaking into a sweat is the fear that we will not get back from the kitchen with our snack before the TV commercial break ends.

Or course, commerce exploits our instinctive tendency to overeat fats and sugars by dressing up products

as 'healthy' or 'nourishing'. Then, having overeaten, we come to resent our ponderous, podgy bodies and so we can be sold diet products.

The answer lies in the mind. More people today feel dissatisfied and unhappy, with far higher numbers suffering depression and compulsions, including eating disorders.

Unhappy people are desperate for a quick fix to make them less miserable. Sugary foods like chocolate act like a drug that temporarily raises spirits.

Our aspirations have far outstripped what it is possible for society to deliver, with women being especially vulnerable. They expect so much more from relationships with lovers and husbands than ever before, while they are encouraged to reach for the sky at work. When neither can match up to these over-stimulated expectations, they feel disappointed and may blame themselves.

These problems exist for the most successful as well. No sooner do we achieve a goal than we move the goalposts to create a new, more difficult one, leaving ourselves permanently dissatisfied, always yearning for what we have not got, a nation of wannabes.

Rancour

At the same time, our attachments are falling apart. Despite their greatly improved opportunities, women are dissatisfied in bed and in the workplace. Men, meanwhile, are confused and reluctant to accept the new status quo.

The result is an unprecedented gender rancour and spiralling divorce rate, at precisely the point in history when we are demanding vastly more from our relationships than ever before.

We are addicts searching for a fix of intensity and intimacy, but ironically, it is the breaking of passionate attachments that is the greatest single cause of despair – the embittered divorcees, the abandoned children, the lonely elderly relatives.

We have not yet discovered a way to encourage every member of society to reach for the sky and yet to avoid selfishness and disappointment when he or she falls to earth.

For the large person, the moral is clear. Until you scale down your ambitions to something more realistic, you will continue to use food (or transfer to another addiction, such as alcohol or gambling or sex) to sweeten the pill of defeat, and your body will continue to grow.

So yes, we are a nation of gluttons. But we are not just gluttons eager to gorge on food. We are gluttons for punishment in the way we are living, lifestyles that consign so many to misery and depression, temporarily banished by a fix of food.

• Oliver James's book, *Britain On The Couch – Why We're Unhappier Compared With 1950 Despite Being Richer*, is published by Century.
© The Daily Mail September, 1997

At last, a little extra weight is growing on us

Britons are becoming comfortable with the comfortable way they look. After years of crash dieting followed by equally rapid weight gain, many are deciding against trying to slim.

Only 38 per cent of people actively cut back on their calorie intake last year – five per cent fewer than in 1994 – analysts Marketpower discovered.

A boom in eating out and takeaways has played a part in the trend.

Fifty-four per cent of those questioned in the survey said they ate whatever they fancied in restaurants without worrying about calories. Marketpower discovered that the most popular dishes eaten outside the home were curries, fried food, chips and pizza – all fattening foods.

Researcher Peter Backman said Britons appeared generally less desperate to be wafer-thin.

'There is a feeling that more people are becoming comfortable with the way they look,' he said. 'They seem to accept that they may be a bit chubby and realise it is their natural shape.

'With the boom in eating out as the country has enjoyed more economic success, people are less fussy about choosing low-calorie dishes in restaurants.

'Eating out is still regarded as a treat and people are more likely to have something like a Black Forest gateau for dessert or something in a creamy sauce for main course. Even people on diets will put them on hold when choosing dishes from a restaurant menu.'

Marketpower says 8.7billion meals were eaten out in Britain last year, compared with 8.3billion five years ago, a boom fuelled by the younger generation.

The biggest increase has been in pubs, hotels and railway stations – places where people are doing something else as well as eating – where the number of meals served has soared by 17 per cent in the past five years, from three billion to 3.5billion. Eating out in restaurants and fast-food outlets has risen by ten per cent from 1.9billion meals in 1991 to 2.1billion last year.

But the number of meals in subsidised locations such s canteens, schools and hospitals dropped from 3.3billion in 1991 to 3.1billion last year.

© The Daily Mail August, 1997

The balance of good health

Information from the Health Education Authority

For most people the move towards a healthy balanced diet means eating more bread, breakfast cereals, potatoes, pasta and rice, and more fruit and vegetables. Above all we should aim for variety in our food.

Bread, other cereals and potatoes

This group includes:
- Bread, rolls, chapattis
- Breakfast cereals, oats
- Pasta, noodles
- Rice
- Potatoes, sweet potatoes
- Dishes made from maise, millet and cornmeal
- Plantains, green bananas
- Beans and lentils

Make these foods the main part of your meals. Eat all types and choose high fibre kinds whenever you can.

Fruit and vegetables

This group includes:
- All fresh, frozen and canned fruit and vegetables
- Salad vegetables
- Beans and lentils

Dried fruit and fruit juice can make up some of the choices from this group.

Try to eat at least five portions of fruit and vegetables each day. Include some vegetables, some salad and some fruit. Choose a wide variety.

Milk and dairy foods

This group includes:
- Milk*
- Cheese*
- Yoghurt*
- Fromage frais*

Meat, fish and alternatives

This group includes:
- Meat – beef, pork, bacon, lamb
- Meat products – sausages,* beefburgers,* meat pies
- Poultry – chicken, turkey

- Fish – fresh, frozen and canned
- Fish products – fish fingers, fish cakes
- Offal – liver, kidney
- Eggs
- Beans and lentils – baked beans, chickpeas, lentils
- Nuts and nut products such as peanut butter
- Textured vegetable protein and other meat alternatives

*Lower fat versions of these foods are available. Choose lower fat alternatives whenever you can.

Foods containing fat; foods containing sugar

This group includes:
Foods we should use sparingly, like:
- Butter
- Margarine
- Low fat spreads
- Cooking oils
- Mayonnaise and oily salad dressings

And foods we can enjoy as treats, like:
- Biscuits
- Cakes
- Puddings
- Ice-cream
- Chocolate
- Sweets
- Crisps
- Sugar
- Sweetened drinks

Try not to eat these too often and when you do, have small amounts.

Some foods such as beans and lentils fit into more than one group because of the mixture of nutrients they contain.

• The above is an extract from *Enjoy Healthy Eating*, produced by the Health Education Authority. See page 41 for details.

© Health Education Authority

MY DOCTOR SAID I SHOULD RUN TEN MILES BEFORE BREAKFAST – SO I GAVE UP HAVING BREAKFAST

America is big loser in battle of the bulge

Fat is transatlantic issue. By Richard Thomas in Washington

American waistlines are expanding relentlessly despite a glut of diet plans, health crazes and personal fitness trainers, according to new research. Health experts say obesity is the second-biggest preventable killer in the United States after smoking.

While a minority of US citizens spend every lunchtime pounding the pavement and every evening sipping health juices, many more are sedentary and fat, the National Centre for Disease Prevention (NCDP) said.

Thirty-five per cent of adults were defined as 'dangerously overweight' in 1994 – up from 25 per cent in 1980, when the last comprehensive survey was conducted.

'The hard data shows us that people are eating more and doing less,' said Sylvia Ogden, who co-ordinated the national survey of 40,000 people. 'So they get fatter.'

Changes in lifestyle which have reduced levels of activity – more car journeys, more office jobs – plus an apparently unstoppable rise in average calorie consumption have pushed more and more Americans into unhealthy obesity, the NCDP said. Black and Mexican-American women are the worst affected, with more than one in two respondents overweight.

Ms Ogden said the findings were in stark contrast to the image of a Lycra-clad, energetic nation. One explanation is that ordinary mortals are intimidated by the regimes of the super-fit. Oprah Winfrey is slim, but she runs five miles a day.

'It is a concern that people will be put off by this kind of thing,' Ms Ogden said.

Overweight children and adolescents have doubled in number as television and computer games take over from football in the street,

and wary parents ban outdoor play.

According to the National Task Force on the Prevention of Obesity, the condition claims 300,000 lives a year and costs $68 billion (£42 billion) in lost working days and lower productivity. Obesity exacerbates heart disease, diabetes and high blood pressure.

Americans spend about $30 billion a year on low-calorie foodstuffs, diet books and kits to help them shed the spare tyres.

Experts warned of the dangers of a diet-binge cycle and said that most weight-reduction plans were ultimately unsuccessful. 'Prevention is better than cure,' Ms Ogden said.

Although most Americans believe radical changes would be needed to stop obesity, the NCDP insisted that modest alterations could make a huge difference.

'It's really important for people not to think that they have to go on strict diets or join gyms,' Ms Ogden said. Thirty minutes a day of walking or gardening would do the trick, she said. 'Basically, just moving around. Using the stairs.'

The NCDP researchers said that while the percentage of fat in Americans' diets had declined in recent years, with food manufacturers competing to display 'low in fat' labels, the drop was outweighed by an increase in the overall amount consumed. If your muffin is fat-free, reasons the typical consumer, why not have two?

Men now consume on average 2,684 calories a day, up from 2,457 in 1980. The average woman's daily calorie intake has jumped from 1,531 to 1,805.

Meanwhile the numbers engaging in physical activity are low: 59 per cent of women and 49 per cent of men report no exercise at all in their weekly routine.

The NCDP survey used a measure of weight and height (the Body Mass Index) to determine which of the 30,000 individuals polled were overweight, and used a generous cut-off point: a 5ft 6in adult would need to weigh more than 12 stone to be defined as overweight, Ms Ogden said. *© The Guardian March, 1997*

Overweight populations

Percentage of the population who are overweight, based on standard Body Mass Index which relates weight to height.

USA	Men	Women
1980	24.2	27.1
1994	33.3	36.4

UK	Men	Women
1980	39	32
1994	56	46

Source: OPCS, NHANES

If you are overweight

An extract from *Enjoy Healthy Eating*, produced by the Health Education Authority

Decrease calories

- Try to fill up on bread, other cereals and potatoes, and on fruit and vegetables – these foods all have less calories and are filling, particularly the wholegrain varieties of starchy foods.
- Cut down on the amount of fat you eat. It has twice as many calories as the same weight of either starch or protein.
- Include lower-fat milk and dairy foods and lean meat, fish and alternatives to make sure that you don't lose out on minerals, vitamins and protein when losing weight.
- Cut out table sugar completely. It gives you 'empty calories', that is, calories with no other nutrients: no vitamins, no minerals, no protein.
- Try to avoid eating foods containing fat and foods containing sugar, such as puddings, biscuits, cakes and chocolate, too often. Replace them with low-fat, low-sugar yoghurt or fresh fruit. Other

foods from this group should be used sparingly – e.g. butter, margarine, low-fat spreads and mayonnaise.

- Avoid sweetened drinks.
- Alcohol has a lot of calories – cut down.

Increase activity

- Walk more – nothing could be simpler. Walk rather than using the bus or car. If you do take the bus then get off one stop before, or after, the one you want, and walk. If you take the car, park a little further from work, the shops or the station. Use the stairs whenever you can.
- Involve the family. Make it into a regular event to get to a park, playground or swimming pool with your family.
- Try to do more activities around the home and garden.
- Try to get involved in some sort of sport. There is a wide variety to choose from.

Remember, a little regular activity can add up to a lot. It is important to be active throughout your life and particularly as you get older, not just when you are trying to lose weight.

• The above is an extract from *Enjoy Healthy Eating*, produced by the Health Education Authority. See page 41 for details.

© Health Education Authority

Overweight nations

Percentage of population who are overweight. Britons are among the fattest people on earth, following only the well-padded Russians and the ample-bottomed Americans. In all three nations, more than half the population have a body mass index over 25, defined as overweight.

Country	% of population
Russia	58
US	55
UK	51
Sweden	42
Colombia	44
Brazil	33
Costa Rica	31
Morocco	22
Togo	18
China	9
India	8
Haiti	7
Senegal	6
Ethiopia	2

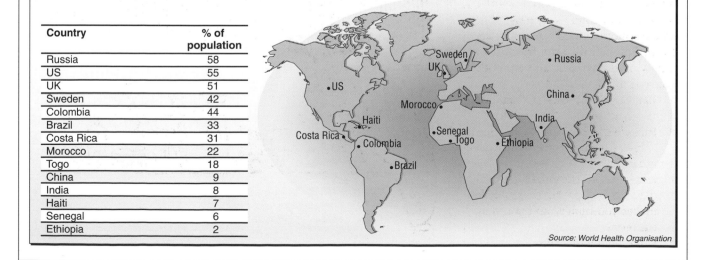

Source: World Health Organisation

Worries about weight

Information from the Royal College of Psychiatrists

Most young people feel dissatisfied with their personal appearance and at times look for ways to change how they look. Many people have an ideal size which they would like to be. Being smaller, shorter, less well-developed than friends or siblings can make you feel anxious and lacking in confidence. So can being teased about your size and weight – which is common among girls.

People's ideas about what looks good are often influenced by others – fashion or friends. Many girls feel they are fat when their weight is in fact within the normal, healthy range for their height. There is actually quite a wide range of sizes and shapes that are within the normal range. Your weight, like height and looks, depends a lot on the type of build your family has.

Maintaining a healthy normal weight

Bodies need regular inputs of energy and nourishment to stay healthy and strong. This is especially important in the teenage years, when the body has to cope with a lot of change and activity. A healthy diet should include a balanced intake of proteins, carbohydrates, fats, minerals and vitamins that are needed for healthy development.

There are some very simple rules which can help maintain a healthy weight. They sound very easy – but can be more difficult to practise. Involving family and friends in following these rules can help both you and them.

- Eat regular meals. Breakfast, lunch, dinner.
- Include carbohydrate foods such as bread, potatoes, rice, pasta with every meal.
- Eat at roughly the same time each day. Long gaps between meals makes you hungry and you may eat more.
- Have sufficient sleep.
- Avoid sugary or high-fat foods and junk foods: a school lunch of crisps, chocolate and a soft drink will increase the risk of weight problems. A sandwich or roll with fruit, milk or juice, is much better for weight control – and your skin.
- Take regular exercise. Walking as a sport or swimming are great for weight control.
- Do not be too influenced by other people skipping meals or commenting on weight.

If you follow these suggestions you will find that weight control is easier, and you will crave less for sweet foods.

'Miracle cures' – do they work?

There are quite a few of these. Sadly, they often do more harm than good.

- Crash diets not only don't help to keep a lower weight, they can even cause weight gain in the long term. At worst, they can be dangerous.
- Exercise helps health. But too much exercise is not an effective or healthy way of staying thin.
- Laxatives may help you feel less guilty and bloated, but do not reduce weight, and can be harmful.
- Appetite suppressants can also harm your health.

Anorexia nervosa, bulimia and other eating disorders

Worry or stress in teenage years may be due to problems or pressures at school, with friends, or at home. Worry or stress can lead to eating foods for comfort, resulting in weight gain and more worry and further need for comfort. These may be foods you enjoy (often fatty or sugary foods). It is useful to monitor your eating habits to make sure that this is not a habit you have slipped into. Sometimes worry and tiredness can lead to loss of appetite.

Unhappiness or stress may lead you to focus on your weight and eating habits in ways that can lead to an eating disorder. The commonest eating disorder is becoming overweight, or obesity. Other eating disorders are less common. Anorexia nervosa and bulimia occur most often among girls, and are discussed below.

If worries have altered your appetite or weight, it will help to talk to someone about it. You should consult your doctor if you are concerned about problems relating to your eating habits and weight.

Signs of an eating disorder

A person with an eating disorder may lose weight or gain weight. In anorexia nervosa the person feels they are fat, and tries to avoid eating,

though the person is not actually overweight. Eating causes uncomfortable feelings of fatness and guilt. So the person avoids food, loses a lot of weight and becomes extremely thin. Strangely, the thinner they get, the fatter they feel! They usually remain very active and say they are quite well, even though they become so thin that they avoid undressing, or wear loose clothes which hide their size. Anorexia nervosa can be dangerous, if it is allowed to take control. A danger sign which means help is needed right away is if a girl's periods stop. (This won't happen if you are on the Pill – so if you are, don't wait for this.)

Avoiding food may lead to episodes of over-eating or 'bingeing'. This is known as bulimia. In bulimia the individual cannot control the desire to eat large amounts of food, especially chocolates, or other fatty foods. They feel fat, guilty and ashamed. They then try to control their weight by vomiting, or using laxatives. Their weight is usually in the normal range, unlike in anorexia. There are a very few people who have anorexia nervosa with bulimic symptoms.

Getting help

If you are worried about your weight or feel you may have an eating disorder you will need to obtain advice and help. There are a number of people who can help with worries about weight or eating problems. These include a family member, teacher, school nurse, counsellor, social worker, or GP. Your family doctor or practice nurse is the best person to give you basic advice on diet and weight. If you need more specialist help, they can refer you to a professional trained to help young people with emotional problems at your local Child and Family Mental Health Service, which is a team of skilled professionals including child psychiatrists, psychologists, social workers, psychotherapists, and specialist nurses. They will respect your wishes for confidentiality. A child and adolescent psychiatrist, for example, will be able to help you to find ways of getting your eating and weight back under control.

Further sources of information

Bryant Waugh, R. & Turner, H. *Eating Disorder: A Parent's Guide*. Published in conjunction with *Bella* Magazine. This book is useful for young people as well as parents.
Young Minds
Helpline 0345 626376.
Eating Disorders Association
Helpline 01603 621414 or 0891 615 466
Youth Helpline 01603 765 050.
© *Royal College of Psychiatrists*

Slimming foods slow to shape up

Six years after the Food Commission's first damning survey of meal replacement slimming foods we ask whether manufacturers are now offering better products. Our new survey finds that not one product yet meets the regulations due to come in early next year.

Back in 1992 we took a close look at meal replacement slimming products – the bars, biscuits and shake mixes sold as aids to slimming. Our survey of 12 leading brands found that products offered poor nutrition; encouraged unhealthy eating habits and promoted unrealistic and unsafe weight loss. Our report formed the basis of a Food Commission submission to the Ministry of Agriculture, Fisheries and Food in which we urged them to support an EU directive aimed at setting nutritional standards for such products and curbing claims on packaging and advertising about weight loss.

Six years later we are pleased to announce that the EU directive has finally become law, although companies have until 31 March 1999 to comply with it. But in a welcome move to speed up compliance, Food Safety Minister Jeff Rooker has urged manufacturers to start following the new rules as soon as possible. In October last year he said: 'Many responsible manufacturers of slimming products already meet these rules. Those that do not will now need to sharpen up their act.'

To discover which companies are 'responsible' and those which are not following Mr Rooker's advice, we took a new look at meal replacement slimming foods to see just what had changed.

What we found
Fewer products
Firstly, we found fewer products on sale in supermarkets and chemists than in our previous surveys – only seven products. Most of the products we found on sale were drink mixes with only one biscuit-type product. Market research company Mintel confirms that a number of products have been withdrawn in recent years.

However, the market for meal replacement products has not declined. According to Mintel, sales of meal replacements increased more than six fold between 1990 and 1995, reaching nearly £74 million, in large part due to the heavy promotion given to leading brands such as Slim Fast. But, despite manufacturers' attempts to persuade would-be slimmers that their products are 'healthy', the popularity of meal replacement foods could face a downturn as the regulations begin to bite.

Nutritional content
The new rules state that products must meet the following nutritional requirements:

Energy: content should be between 200-400kcals per 'meal'.

Protein: must make up 25 – 50% of energy.

Fat: must constitute no more than 30% of energy.

Vitamins and minerals: each 'meal' must contain at least 30% of specified amounts of 23 vitamins and minerals.

Despite these long-anticipated requirements we were disappointed to find no significant nutritional improvements since our last survey. None of the products in our survey met the nutritional requirements of the forthcoming rules in every respect.

We found:
- All but two of the products would meet the fat requirement. The exceptions are Crunch and Slim with 44% of energy from fat – far higher than the 30% that will be permitted – and Complan with just over 30% when made up with water.
- Two out of seven products would fail to meet the energy requirements. Both NutraSlim and Thigh and Hip Slim have fewer than 200 kcals per serving.
- Three out of seven products would fail to meet the protein requirements. Crunch and Slim, SlimFast ready-to-drink and Complan contain too little protein.
- Three out of seven products would fail to meet the vitamin and mineral requirements: Crunch and Slim has too little iron, Slimma Shake has inadequate levels of vitamins A and D and biotin while Complan fails to provide adequate levels of nine vitamins and minerals.
- Although the EC directive includes no requirements for sugar, we found all products were high in sugar – in five out of the seven products over half the calories are from sugar.

Fluid intake
The new rules will also mean that products must warn of the importance of maintaining an adequate daily fluid intake. We found that three products – Thigh and Hip Slim, Complan and NutraSlim – do not currently do so.

Claims
Products will no longer be able to make any reference in their labelling, advertising or presentation 'to the rate or amount of weight loss which may result from its use'. Furthermore, products must not refer to 'a reduction in the sense of hunger or an increase in the sense of satiety'.

We found six out of the seven products make references to the rate or amount of weight loss. Slimfast and NutraSlim refer to 'fast' weight loss, Slimma Shake refers to 'quick' weight control (although it was ambiguous as to whether this referred to weight loss or preparation time) and Crunch and Slim claims you could 'lose up to 6lbs in your first week'.

Worse still is the claim made for Thigh and Hip Slim, which carries the testimony 'I went from dress size 18 to size 10 in just 9 and a half weeks.' Although called Thigh and Hip Slim the product says in the small print that the product will not especially help you lose weight from your thighs or hips. Trading Standards Officers have told the Food Commission that the restrictions on claims will also cover names of products, so it is likely that SlimFast will need to change its name to stay within the law.

Crunch and Slim would also fall foul of the rules for claiming that the product will 'fill you up, providing long lasting satisfaction'. Only Complan would meet the forthcoming claims requirement.

Our conclusion
All companies in our survey have some way to go to meet the requirements of the new rules. Apart from the nutritional inadequacies highlighted here, meal replacement foods are not a highly recommended way of losing and maintaining weight. They do little to re-educate slimmers' eating habits, and make it all too easy to return to poor habits once dieting is stopped – thus encouraging unhealthy yo-yo dieting. For this reason many labels recommend slimmers to keep on using the products indefinitely.

Who are the 'responsible' manufacturers who already comply with the directive? Slim Fast told us they were planning a new formulation. Otherwise, we found that the manufacturers of all the products we surveyed need, in the words of Jeff Rooker, to 'sharpen up their act'.

• The above is an extract from *The Food Magazine*, published by the Food Commission. See page 41 for address details.

© *The Food Magazine*

Let children eat crisps, says doctor

Society's obsession with healthy eating and exercise is driving children to anorexia. Chocolate, crisps and chips are good for people, a leading expert in eating disorders said yesterday. Judith Judd, Education Editor, explains why Dr Dee Dawson wants children to eat Mars bars rather than celery sticks.

Around half of six-year-old girls are worried about their weight. Between 1 and 2 per cent of girls are anorexic and 5 per cent of sixth-formers are bulimic. Dr Dee Dawson, medical director of the Rhodes Farm Clinic in London, told heads of leading girls' independent schools that we must stop making children feel guilty about food.

Dr Dawson recently had a six-year-old in her clinic who was crying and refusing to eat because her thighs were too fat, she said at the Girls' Schools Association annual conference in Bristol. Society, she said, should be ridiculing the muscle-wasted models of fashion magazines and pointing out that page three girls in the *Sun* newspaper did not look like that.

'Marilyn Monroe was at least a size 16, as indeed are 47 per cent of the female population,' she said.

'The media, the fashion industry, teachers, parents and the Government all played a part in ruining some children's lives by endless talk about the evils of fat. Chocolate, cheese, crisps and chips are wonderful energy-giving foods which children need. Almost without exception my patients are fat phobic.'

Almost all had been putting water on their cereals before they were admitted, she added. One would not go swimming in case, she said, she absorbed fat from fat people in the water. Teachers should not tell children that a low-fat diet was healthy, and mothers should not eat salad in front of their children and snack on cheesecake and ice-cream when they were in bed.

Advice being prepared by the Government on children's diet and leaked recently was wrong, she argued. It is said to recommend banning school tuck shops, banning chips from school canteens and restricting chocolate sales from vending machines. Government advice on school meals published earlier this year already advises restricting fat intake. But Dr Dawson said there was not a shred of evidence to suggest that children should avoid fat.

'I would like to say to the Government: think twice before you panic yet more children into a life of chronic starvation and possible death,' she said.

Parents and schools could do more to help, she believes. Parents needed to face up more readily to their children's eating disorders. Schools should weigh all pupils every term and those about whom they were worried every week without divulging the results, she suggested.

Isabel Raphael, head of Channing School in north-east London, said that the fashion industry was partly to blame for girls' worries about their weight. 'I have had perfectly normal developing girls in my room who say they can't go to the local shopping centre with their friends because they can't find anything fashionable that fits,' she said.

Penelope Penney of the Haberdashers' Aske's Girls School in Hertfordshire, said her school was considering weighing all girls in the third year but it would be difficult to organise it more than twice a year.

© The Independent
November, 1997

Early-death warning for the obese

One in five adults risks an early death because of obesity, an expert warned yesterday. But many of those at risk are unlikely to be helped because doctors and patients are not on the same wavelength.

Professor Tony Winder, of the Royal Free Hospital in Hampstead, London, claims that while doctors and other health workers are concerned about the health risks associated with obesity, such as stroke, heart disease, diabetes and osteoarthritis, patients are more worried about the low self-esteem which often comes with being fat and the possible loss of their social lives.

'We all know that fat people eat more than they need, although that may still not seem much,' he said. 'The question is – what are we going to do about it and who is going to take the lead? First we have to get the patients and health people on the same wavelength, then to establish team systems for working with patients on their problems.' The subject of how obesity should be treated was to be debated at the hospital yesterday.

© The Independent
September, 1997

ADDITIONAL RESOURCES

You might like to contact the following organisations for further information. Due to the increasing cost of postage, many organisations cannot respond to enquiries unless they receive a stamped, addressed envelope.

Association for the Study of Obesity
20 Brook Meadow Close
Woodford Green
Essex, IG8 9NR
Tel: 0181 503 2042
Promotes medical research into the causes, prevention and treatment of obesity. Facilitates contact between individuals and organisations interested in any aspect of the problem of obesity and body weight regulation. Produces publications.

British Nutrition Foundation (BNF)
High Holborn House
52-54 High Holborn
London, WC1V 6RQ
Tel: 0171 404 6504
The BNF is an independent charity which provides reliable information and advice on nutrition and related health matters. They produce a wide range of leaflets, briefing papers and books. Ask for their publications list.

ChildLine
2nd Floor Royal Mail Building
Studd Street
London, N1 0QW
Tel: 0171 239 1000 (admin)
A free, national helpline for young people in trouble or danger. Provides confidential phone counselling service for any child with any problem 24 hours a day. Produces publications. Children or young people can phone or write free of charge about problems of any kind to: ChildLine, Freepost 1111, London N1 0BR, Tel: Freephone 0800 1111

Eating Disorders Association (EDA)
1st Floor, Wensum House
103 Prince of Wales Road
Norwich
Norfolk, NR1 1DW
Tel: 01603 619090
Offers support and mutual self care to those suffering from anorexia and bulimia nervosa and their families through phone helplines, a network of self-help groups, information and newsletters. Produces publications.

First Steps to Freedom
22 Randall Road
Kenilworth
Warwickshire, CV8 1JY
Helpline: 01926 851608
Offers advice, support and counselling to people who suffer from phobias, general anxiety, obsessional compulsive disorders, and their carers. Produces publications.

Health Education Authority – HQ
Trevelyan House
30 Great Peter Street
London, SW1P 2HW
Tel: 0171 222 5300
Fax: 0171 413 8900
Provides free advice for people on all health issues, including anorexia and bulimia.

Maisner Centre For Eating Disorders
Box 464
Hove, BN3 3UG
Tel: 01273 729818
Deals with bulimia and compulsive eating. Offers personal consultations.

MIND
Granta House
15-19 Broadway
London, E15 4BQ
Tel: 0181 519 2122
MIND is a leading mental health charity in England and Wales. They produce a wide range of advice leaflets (45p each), reports and books. Also produce the magazine *Open Mind*.

Office of Health Economics
12 Whitehall
London, SW1A 2DY
Tel: 0171 930 9203
Publishes a useful book called *Eating Disorders: Anorexia Nervosa and Bulimia Nervosa*, 1994 by Richard West. Cost £5.00. Suitable for further/higher education courses and professionals in the health care field.

Overeaters Anonymous
PO Box 19
Stretford
Manchester, M32 9EB
Tel: 01426 984674
Welcomes those with all types of eating disorder, offering identification and acceptance. Works to relieve our compulsion to overeat/undereat, or an obsession with food/dieting by living by spiritual principles based on the 12 steps of Alcoholics Anonymous. Produces publications.

Royal College of Psychiatrists
17 Belgrave Square
London, SW1X 8PG
Tel: 0171 235 2351
Fax: 0171 245 1231
Produces an excellent series of free leaflets on various aspects of mental health. Supplied free of charge but a stamped, addressed envelope is required.

The Food Commission
94 White Lion Street
London, N1 9PF
Tel: 0171 837 2250
Fax: 0171 837 1141
Provides education, information, advice and research on nutrition, diet, health and food production. Runs various educational and research campaigns, publishes *Food Magazine* and other publications.

Young Minds
102-108 Clerkenwell Road
London, EC1M 5SA
Tel: 0171 336 8445
Young Minds, the national association for children's mental health. Produces a range of leaflets, reports, a magazine and newsletters.

INDEX

adolescents *see* young people
age, and eating disorders 1, 6, 9, 11, 13
anorexia athletica (compulsive exercising) 11
anorexia nervosa 1, 4-5, 37-8
    age of sufferers 9, 13
    characteristics of sufferers 4
    defining 4
    and family relationships 5
    incidence of 4, 9, 11
    and medical intervention 10, 15, 38
    personal experience of 8-10
    psychological factors 4
    recovery from 4
    right to starve themselves 10, 15
    self-perception of the anorexic 4-5, 10
    symptoms 4
    treatment 5

binge eating disorder 20-2
    causes 20
    characteristics of sufferers 20-1
    and dieting 20, 21
    diseases caused by 20
    personal experiences of 21-2
    symptoms 20
    treatment 21
Body Mass Index 35
body weight
    and dieting 18
    healthy 26
    overweight people 35
    see also obesity
boys
    and eating disorders 1
bulimia nervosa 1, 6-7, 38
    and binge eating disorder 20, 21
    causes of 6
    health dangers 6-7
    incidence of 11
    and men 13, 14
    self-help for 19
    symptoms 7
    treatment 7
    and young women 13
    see also binge eating disorder

calories
    average daily consumption 35
    and physical activity 29
children, and eating disorders 1, 40
compulsive eating 1
    binge eating disorder 20-22
compulsive exercising (anorexia athletica) 11

death
    from eating disorders 9, 11
        rights of anorexics 15
depression
    and eating disorders 7, 14, 20, 21
    and obesity 24
dieting
    and binge eating disorder 20, 21
    and body weight 18

    and bulimia 19
    crash diets 37
    eating disorders triggered by 3
    low-fat diets 19, 27, 35
    myths 17-19
    rapid weight-loss programmes 18
eating disorders 1-23, 37-8
    biological factors 2
    and children 1, 40
    family factors 2-3
    geography and socio-economic factors 13
    helping a friend or relative with 12-13
    incidence of 11
    and men 3, 11, 13, 14, 22
    mortality rates 11
    psychological factors 2
    recovery from 11, 13
    self-help for 19
    social factors 3
    see also anorexia nervosa; binge eating disorders; bulimia
        nervosa
exercise
    aerobic activity 30
    and bulimia nervosa 20
    compulsive exercising (anorexia athletica) 11
    and obesity 25, 32
    and weight control 29-31, 35, 36, 37

family relationships, and eating disorders 1, 2-3, 5, 6
fasting, and bulimia nervosa 20

girls
    and eating disorders 1, 4, 8-10, 11, 13, 14
    see also young people

health benefits, of physical activity 29-30
health risks
    binge eating disorder 20
    bulimia nervosa 6-7
healthy eating 34, 36, 37
    and children 40

meal replacement slimming products 38-9
medical intervention, and eating disorders 10, 15, 38
men
    calorie consumption 35
    and compulsive overeating 22
    and eating disorders 1, 3, 11, 13, 14
    and obesity 24
    thin and overweight 27
    and waist size 28

obesity 24-40
    and binge eating disorder 20
    causes of 24, 32-3
    defining 24
    health risks associated with 24-5, 28, 32, 35, 40
    and medication to lose weight 25-6
    overweight nations 36
    statistics 32

parents
    of anorexics 5, 8-10
    children and diet 40

 of compulsive overeating victims 21
 of friends with eating disorders 12-13
 and obesity 24
personality, and eating disorders 2, 4, 7
purging, and bulimia nervosa 20

self-help
 for binge eating disorder 21
 for eating disorders 19
starvation
 medical effects of 9
 and the rights of anorexics 15
suicide, and eating disorders 15

teenagers *see* young people
thinness
 gay men and 14
 and teenagers 16
 thin men 27
 women and 3, 11

vomiting, and bulimia nervosa 1, 6-7, 20
weight control
 and physical activity 29-31, 35, 36, 37
 see also dieting
Weight-control Information Network (WIN) 20-1, 29-31
women
 and anorexia nervosa 4, 9
 athletes and eating disorders 23
 and binge eating disorder 20
 and bulimia nervosa 11
 calorie consumption 35
 and eating disorders 13
 expectations of 33
 pressure to be thin 3, 11

young people
 and body image 16, 37, 40
 and eating disorders 1, 37-8
young women, and eating disorders 1, 11, 13

Independence Web News

Back | Forward | Home | Reload | Images | Open | Print | Find | Stop

Live Home Page | Search | Computer | Support | System

The Internet has been likened to shopping in a supermarket without aisles. The press of a button on a Web browser can bring up thousands of sites but working your way through them to find what you want can involve long and frustrating on-line searches. And unfortunately many sites contain inaccurate, misleading or heavily biased information. Our researchers have therefore undertaken an extensive analysis to bring you a selection of quality Web site addresses. If our readers feel that this new innovation in the series is useful, we plan to provide a more extensive Web site section in each new book in the *Issues* series.

* * * * *

ANRED (Anorexia Nervosa and Related Eating Disorders, Inc.)
www.anred.com
Their web site has detailed information about anorexia nervosa, bulimia nervosa, binge eating disorder, and other less well known eating and weight disorders. Their site includes details about recovery and prevention.

Conde Naste
www.phys.com
A site which covers most aspects of fitness and nutrition in a light-hearted manner. Quizzes help ascertain whether you are fit enough to exercise, what your eating personality is and the sort of exercise ideally suited to you.

Dr. Michael Myers
www.weight.com
Provides objective medical information on obesity, weight control, eating disorders and other related medical conditions.

Eating Disorders Association (EDA)
www.gurney.org.uk/eda
An essential site to visit for anyone wanting detailed UK based information on eating disorders: case studies, advice/ help, poems, reading lists etc.

Obesity.com
www.obesity.com
Dedicated to providing practical, up-to-the-minute information about weight loss and obesity. The site provides practical information that supports healthy and practical weight management and weight loss.

Royal College of Psychiatrists
www.rcpsych.ac.uk
They have produced an award winning series of leaflets called *Help is at hand* (one leaflet gives detailed information on eating disorders). Now available on their web site.

Shape Up America
www.shapeup.org
This web site is designed to provide you with the latest information about safe weight management and physical fitness. You can explore the different areas of the site by clicking on one of the interactive 'rooms'.

Something Fishy Web Site on Eating Disorders
www.something-fishy.com/ed.htm
Contains a vast amount of information, on anorexia, bulimia, overeating and other eating disorders. Mostly US based information, lots of links to other relevant sites. Well worth a visit.

ACKNOWLEDGEMENTS

The publisher is grateful for permission to reproduce the following material.

While every care has been taken to trace and acknowledge copyright, the publisher tenders its apology for any accidental infringement or where copyright has proved untraceable. The publisher would be pleased to come to a suitable arrangement in any such case with the rightful owner.

Chapter One: Eating Disorders

Eating problems, © ChildLine, January 1996, *What causes eating disorders?*, © Anorexia Nervosa and Related Eating Disorders Inc. (ANRED), 1997, *My teenage diet hell*, by Ginger Spice, © The Daily Mail, March 1998, *Anorexia nervosa*, © Eating Disorders Association, January 1998, *Bulimia nervosa*, © Eating Disorders Association, January 1998, *Anorexia – and the disturbing problem no parent can ignore*, © The Daily Mail, October 1997, *How many people have eating and exercise disorders?*, © Anorexia Nervosa and Related Eating Disorders Inc. (ANRED), 1997, *Helping a friend or a relative*, © Eating Disorders Association, *Who gets eating disorders?*, © New York Online Access to Health (NOAH website), June 1998, *Thin end of the Reg*, © The Guardian, September 1997, *Anorexics 'should be allowed to starve'*, © The Daily Mail, July 1997, *Slim equals beautiful in the minds of most teenagers*, © The Daily Mail, October 1997, *15 diet myths exploded*, © Woman's Journal, June 1998, *Binge eating disorders*, © Weight-control Information Network (WIN), February 1998, *Compulsive overeating and binge eating disorders*, © Something Fishy, 1998, *Athletes and eating disorders*, © Colleen Thompson, 1998.

Chapter Two: Obesity

Obesity, © Anorexia Nervosa and Related Eating Disorders Inc. (ANRED), 1997, *Are you a healthy weight?*, © Health Education Authority, *Chunky chaps*, © The Daily Mail, June 1997, *It's not how fat a fellow is, it's where he's fat*, © The Daily Mail, September 1997, *Physical activity and weight control*, © Weight-control Information Network (WIN), February 1998, *Meat eaters are more likely to be obese*, © Imperial Cancer Research Fund, September 1996, *The real reason so many of us are overweight*, © The Daily Mail, September 1997, *At last, a little extra weight is growing on us*, © The Daily Mail, August 1997, *The balance of good health*, © Health Education Authority, *America is big loser in battle of the bulge*, © The Guardian, March 1997, *Overweight populations*, © OPCS, NHANES, *If you are overweight*, © Health Education Authority, *Overweight nations*, © World Health Organisation, *Worries about weight*, © Royal College of Psychiatrists, *Slimming foods slow to shape up*, © Food Magazine, *Let children eat crisps, says doctor*, © The Independent, November 1997, *Early-death warning for the obese*, © The Independent, September 1997.

Photographs and illustrations:

Pages 1, 7, 8, 10, 12, 22, 39: The Attic Publishing Co., pages 15, 16, 27, 32, 34: Ken Pyne, pages 16, 18, 24: Ralf Ziegermann, pages 37: Katherine Fleming.

Thank you

Darin Jewell for assisting in the editorial research for this publication.

Craig Donnellan
Cambridge
September, 1998